To

Love and Be

Mary Holmes is retired and attained an English Literature degree with the Open University when she was sixty. She lives in Nottinghamshire and has been married to Tony for forty one years. They have two children, two grandsons and three granddaughters. Mary is passionate about saving local wildlife and is a devotee of Charles Dickens and Rock'n'Roll.

BEING YOU

Mary E. Holmes

BEING YOU

AUSTIN MACAULEY

A CIP catalogue record for this title is
available from the British Library.

ISBN 978 1 905609 24-6

www.austinmacauley.com

First Published (2008)
Austin & Macauley Publishers Ltd.
25 Canada Square
Canary Wharf
London
E14 5LB

Printed & Bound in Great Britain

Dedication

For Elaine without whom this story could not be told.

For Tony who gave me the confidence to write it.

Acknowledgements

I'd like to express my gratitude to Professor Tom Bouchard Jr. and Dr Nancy Segal, not just for being wonderful characters who supplied me with excellent material for this story, but also for caring and giving me so much encouragement during the publishing procedure.

To Chief Editor Annette, to David, Ross, Max and Gemma at Austin & Macauley for guiding me through the publishing process with kindness and humanity. A special thank you to Frances for her hard work on my behalf.

To all my friends near and far whose ears must be heaving a sigh of relief.

To my family, particularly Lisa, Paul, Steven, Julie, Martin, Tasha, Ethan, Aeron and Darcie who have listened and supported all my highs and lows whilst writing this book.

To Elaine for being Elaine. Last but not least, my dear husband Tony for his artwork for the book and the suffering he has endured for the sake of my art.

Foreword

by

Nancy L. Segal, Ph.D.
Department of Psychology and Twin Studies Center
California State University
800 N. State College Blvd.
Fullerton, CA 92834
USA

Author:

Entwined Lives: Twins and What They Tell Us About Human Behavior
(2000, NY: Plume)

Indivisible by Two: Lives of Extraordinary Twins
(2007, Cambridge, MA: Harvard University Press)

What a powerful, wonderful and insightful book! Mary Holmes has beautifully captured the longing for an identical twin sister she never knew, as well as those first marvelous moments of meeting. Once reunited, the twins' closeness came quickly and effortlessly and continues to this day. The reader feels as though he or she is truly there, experiencing the highs and lows along with her.

I met Mary and her twin sister, Elaine, in 1984 when they participated in the Minnesota Study of Twins Reared Apart, at the University of Minnesota. Reunited identical and fraternal twins were invited to the campus for an intensive, week-long battery of psychological and medical testing. Individually and collectively, these pairs are research treasures, allowing us to see the extent to which genes and environments affect our physical and behavioral development. As a member of the research team, I administered many of the protocols to Mary and Elaine, and to other twins. Mary recounts her research experiences during that week, and it was both informative and fun to watch it through her eyes.

The social relationship that evolves between reared apart twins has fascinated me more than anything else about them. Many of identical pairs show a natural comfort and ease with one another that is remarkable, given their years apart. Some also display an array of childlike tendencies (e.g., wearing the same outfits, playing jokes on the investigators) as if making up for their missed childhood years. Meeting a twin is clearly a life-changing event, replete with new in-laws, nieces and nephews, and information about one's past. The first letters, conversations and meetings between two identical beings would seem to be indescribable, yet Mary brings them clearly to life. She brilliantly conveys the anxiety and uncertainty that precedes that first reunion, and the joy and relief that follows. All this affirms our belief in the importance of family and will, no doubt, remind twins everywhere how lucky they are to have one another. For separated twins, this book will be a difficult reminder of the happiness they have been denied, but may one day hope to find. But *Being You* is about more than meeting one's twin.

Being You is also about confronting the past, discovering hidden talents and exploring new interests. Identical twins, especially those reared apart, are in the unique position of seeing themselves in a life not lived. Mary's mother adopted her only after Elaine's parents decided that they could not afford to take both twins. This turn of events had major consequences for the lives each twin would lead—and this is why the book will have such universal appeal. Everyone feels the effects of choices made by others, yet only one outcome can be known. Mary can also wonder, "What if Elaine's family's circumstances had been more favorable . . . ?" But she can turn to her twin for answers.

Being You might have been called *Being Yourself* because, together, Mary and Elaine brought out the best in one another—and still do.

Nancy L. Segal, Ph.D.

Unique and Alike

Professor Thomas J Bouchard, Jr
Professor of Psychology
Director: Minnesota Center for Twin and Adoption Research
University of Minnesota Minneapolis, MA

My colleagues and I studied monozygotic (identical) twins reared apart for over twenty years. Mary and Elaine were one of the series of twin pairs who visited our laboratories. The result of our studies has been a long list of scientific papers filled with quantitative analyses - one set of numbers after another. Our reading of the numbers led us to the conclusion that monozygotic twins reared apart were far more similar on far more psychological traits (personality,abilities,interests,social   attitudes   etc)   than psychologists had believed possible. Indeed monozygotic twins reared apart turned out to be about as similar as monozygotic twins reared together. Each twin is unique but also alike. Monozygotic twins reared together are 50% similar, however, reared apart twins are also 50% similar. This suggests a very large but certainly less than fully deterministic genetic influence on psychological traits. These results are both surprising and not surprising at all. The fact that twins reared apart are just as similar as twins reared together also tells us that being raised in the same family is much less a cause of similarity in twins than psychologists previously thought. This is a surprising fact as psychologists have long believed that the reason monozygotic twins are so similar is because parents treat them so similarly. The evidence suggests the reason for similarity is "genetic factors."

How do all these dry facts relate to Mary's story? That's an easy question to answer. Her vivid story gives real life to the scientists' beloved numbers. Reading this story leaves no doubt that Mary and Elaine are different people who had lived very different lives and accumulated many different experiences. Each is a unique person. Despite different experiences they are similar in a great many ways. How do genes cause psychological similarity? The truth is we don't know. One theory, which I like, is that genetic factors influence, in important ways, what we pay attention to and what we think about. In other words, "to a considerable degree people make their own internal and external environments." In spite of the way her mother treated her, Mary thought about things in "her way." I have little doubt Elaine would have told the same story. Twins reared apart present us with a number of mysteries and make it clear that we have a great deal to learn about the causes of human behaviour.

Mary's story also highlights the role of chance in human affairs. After a number of missed opportunities, chance led Mary to Elaine. Other twins in our study were also re-united as a result of chance events, but we also accumulated numerous cases of twins in search of their co-twin who were never reunited. Some twins are luckier than others. This is the story of a lucky pair.

This is a wonderful human story. Read it - you will love it!

Professor Thomas J Bouchard, Jr

PART ONE

We shared a womb for nine months,
a drawer for two, and nothing for thirty years.

Chapter One

The day I discovered the existence of another me it was raining and we were shopping for a nit comb. At school a nurse had raked my head with bony fingers, uttered something unintelligible and barked "next". The consequence of which, left me stumbling over wet cobblestones, my hand clamped firmly in my mother's vice-like grip.

'Stop scratching, I've told you it'll make it worse.'

I looked up at my mother and saw the grim line of her mouth as she pulled me along. With my free hand I surreptitiously moved my beret from side to side.

'What have I just said…'

Her tirade fell to the floor along with the rain, as my eyes fastened onto a large black and white photograph posted on the front of our local cinema. It glowed like a bright star against the drab brickwork. It wasn't the beautiful face of the film star which held me spellbound, but the little girl sitting in front of her; it was me. Even with long hair which fell into ringlets – I wasn't allowed long hair in case I got nits – her face was mine. Despite the shimmering white dress the protruding knobbly knees matched mine. I dragged my feet in an attempt to slow our progress along the street. My mother looked down at me suspiciously.

'What's the matter, do you need the lavatory?'

'No.' I replied in a small voice.

'Well move yourself, I haven't got all day.'

'Can I just look at that picture of me?' I pleaded, desperately wanting to glory in this sudden stardom. 'Please.'

Suddenly the grip relaxed on my arm as my mother came to an abrupt halt. She leaned forward wiping her nose energetically whilst peering intently at the photograph. When she straightened up she had a strange look on her face. I was accustomed to her stern facial expressions, but she seemed uneasy; as if she feared the picture. Then she said dismissively.

'Don't be silly. How could it possibly be you?' She tugged at my hand and off we went down the rain-slicked street at a brisk pace, as if to put as much space between us and the offending image. My mother was right. Even though I yearned for it to be me, how could it? I was a five-year-old little girl; with nits.

My only claim to fame that day was having my head scraped with a lethal-looking metal comb, until my scalp stung. If the harsh metal was intended to obliterate the impression from my head then it almost worked, but a blurry picture would occasionally jump into my mind like a subliminal image; and then I would remember.

* * *

Ostensibly, I was a small, timid child, but crammed with an imagination the size of Australia. This was not well received by my mother, who sniffed loudly and complained vociferously about my shortcomings. Her voice would pursue me around the house.

'Have you got your nose stuck in a book again?'

'If you got your head out of the clouds you would hear me when I'm talking to you.'

'Haven't you finished washing those dishes yet?'

Even though I feared the sound of my mother's voice, my clouds would still convey me into the exciting fictional lives of the characters who inhabited the pages of books, either given to me or borrowed from the library. Much of the reading material was of a religious nature, but I was not easily deterred. When I was eight years old something happened which surpassed the fictional stories, and I began to wonder if it was figment of my fanciful imagination. Could I have imagined my visits to the doctors? No, they were too frequent, as was the bed-wetting. Something best forgotten but unfortunately a memory which has accompanied me through life like a battle scar. I recall trying everything to remedy this stain on my character; not to mention the bed. I would drink nothing except the obligatory bottle of school milk. On the point of dehydration I prayed fervently to my Catholic God, but all I achieved were ugly, red marks on my bony knees.

The doctor's waiting room was full of people sniffing and coughing; an aura of gloom cloaked them like an invisible blanket. Every seat was occupied and, sighing audibly, my mother stood by the door whilst I surveyed the yellowing copies of *The People's Friend* hopefully. Suddenly, a little girl bounced up to me smiling broadly.

'Hello, do you want to play?'

She seemed to take a great liking to me, and for some inexplicable reason kept calling me Elaine. I began to wonder if perhaps I'd been cast as the heroine in some exciting story she'd created to alleviate the boredom of the surgery, but when she told her mother she was "playing with Elaine" my confusion multiplied. I knew my name was Mary Elizabeth, because I had been named after the Virgin Mary and was expected to, if not exactly, follow in her footsteps, at least behave accordingly; in this respect I was a great disappointment to my parents. My new-found friendship was, however, short-lived, and before I could even say goodbye, let alone unravel the mystery, I was hurried into the surgery and never saw her again.

Later that day, I was summoned to the front room, a room so particular in every detail it was used only for special occasions. Sunlight spilled in through a large bay window and

21

settled sedately on the radio console making the walnut wood gleam. Three highly coloured geese flew dangerously up one wall on the point of colliding horribly with the ceiling. Everything in the room, including the geese, had to be cleaned and polished all to the standard of which my mother would have approved. I squirmed silently on the edge of a chair awaiting my fate. What had I done? What had I not done? The chant started in my head and ended in a tight knot in my stomach.

It looked serious. The whole family were assembled in the room. Strangely, my mother still wore her outdoor hat, the colour had changed over the years but the severe shapes stayed the same. The front edge was straight and unforgiving, wedged over her forehead, totally covering her brown hair. It gave her face an uncompromising profile. I suppose I viewed her in terms of shapes; depending upon her mood her angular body and sensible shoes could fill a room like a storm cloud which hadn't decided whether to burst loudly or grumble quietly.

By contrast, my father was small with thinning, fair hair and a kind face, which was lined and furrowed from long hours working in the foundry. My sister, Ann, was staring out of the window watching dark clouds momentarily chase away the sun. She was ten years older than me, all but one day, but there the similarity ended. She had cornflower blue eyes, hair the colour of ripened wheat, a curvaceous body and placid nature. Whereas, my eyes were almost as dark as my ebony hair, I was small and skinny with a strong character which screamed for release; but knew its place. In retrospect, it seems strange that I never questioned why I was so dissimilar to everyone else in the household, why there seemed an otherness about me which didn't fit in. Perhaps when you're a child you accept anomalies without question; so although I often felt I'd wandered into the wrong house, I wouldn't have dared put voice to this peculiar thought; besides which, I was generally too occupied keeping out of trouble.

We all seemed to be waiting. Dad was looking at me kindly; which could mean I was really in trouble. Often, when faced with my mother's disapproval over some misdemeanour, he would come to my defence and... my mother's voice jerked me back to the present.

'You know when we were at the doctor's today?'

The severity of the knot in my stomach increased; it must be about my bed-wetting. I fidgeted in the chair thinking about my punishment, but all I said was, 'Yes.'

'Well,' my mother continued, 'there was a little girl who kept calling you Elaine, did you wonder why?'

Oh joy, it didn't sound too bad. But wait a minute, if I start saying I thought I was part of some make-believe story, it might turn into a 'she's got her head in the clouds again', episode. After hesitating I said.

'Er, no, not really, she must have thought I was someone else.'

Good answer, my mother's face brightened.

'Yes, that's exactly right, she thought you were someone else.'

Was I supposed to ask who? I said nothing. As the minutes lengthened, everyone looked at me expectantly. My father cleared his throat.

'There's something we've to tell you lass, it's best you should know now, so you don't get confused, like.' Before he could continue my mother interjected.

'We adopted you when you were a baby, you're not like our Ann, she was our own, but we actually chose to have you because your own mother didn't want you and we gave you a home.' My mother paused, maybe to let this sink in. Actually I did know what being adopted meant because my best friend

Stella had been adopted, a little nugget I was about to impart; but before I could speak she continued.

'When we adopted you there were two babies and the other one was your twin sister, Elaine. The people who adopted her never changed her name. Goodness knows why not; we wouldn't have dreamed of keeping the non-Catholic name you had.' My mother's tone had taken on an indignant righteousness. 'Anyway, that's why the little girl in the doctors kept calling you Elaine, because I expect you look alike.' She finished, folding her arms across her chest.

Aloud, all that came out of my mouth was 'Oh.' Silently, my head teemed with questions. Where is this twin sister? Can I see her? Can I play with her? Does she live far away? What is my real name? This was the most exciting thing that had happened to me since I'd fallen off my tricycle, down a bank and into the river below; well it was a stream really. Then my dreams fell to the floor with a thud.

'Obviously, we've had to tell you now because of that girl, but we think a clean break from your past will be better for everyone. We made sure that Elaine wasn't sent to the same school.' My mother sniffed. 'Course it didn't bother them, they're supposed to be Catholics, but they don't go to church much and I insisted you would have to attend St .Mary's Catholic School. If we hadn't adopted you, you would have gone into a children's home, because *they* wouldn't have you.'

Who wouldn't have me?

Whilst my mother paused for breath I asked a more pressing question and one which was unpardonable. 'Will I be able to play with Elaine?'

My mother glared. 'Most certainly not, I've just told you if you'd been listening. We're your family now and just as well from what I've heard, they let her do just what she pleases; running around dancing on stage and goodness knows what else. No good will come of it, she'll end up a bad lot, you mark my words.' She paused, and I tried to imagine being Elaine.

Contrary to my mother's intentions I felt exhilarated at the thought. Meanwhile my mother pursued her point.

'Mind you, I'm not in the least bit surprised. They made sure they took the biggest baby before we even got there; and the best baby clothes. Course, they knew your real mother, she was a Jewess.'

Jewess? What's a Jewess?

A heavy silence pervaded the room. My mother had stopped speaking and sat back in her chair with a satisfied air about her, as if her final sentence explained everything. But I was more bewildered then than I had ever been in all of my eight years.

Chapter Two

The minutes crawled by. The loud tick of the wooden clock seated on the mantle above the fireplace punctuated the silence like a time bomb.

'Well now you've been told, haven't you got anything to say?'

Questions I didn't dare to ask jostled for position in my head, instead I said, 'Where did you get me from?' Did I think they'd purchased me at the local shop together with a loaf and a pound of butter? I don't know what I thought or what I felt. I knew how to feel when I was in trouble, but this outpouring of information confused me. How was I supposed to feel? How was I to react with a family whom I didn't belong, but belonged to?

In spite of this, as the information began to take root inside me, I felt the otherness being replaced by a warm glow which sprang from within, it made me feel special, special because I had a twin sister; but somehow special had metamorphosed into sin. My friends and I always struggled to find enough sins to confess every week in the confessional box, and wild images began to run riot inside my head.

'Forgive me father for I have sinned. This week I discovered I have a twin sister. She apparently hasn't got a Catholic name, she dances and runs around doing goodness knows what, and I asked if I could play with her.'

A sharp intake of breath, the fine gauze curtain covering the mesh grille gently swings as the priest exhales, and I catch a glimpse of his black cassock and stiff white collar which looks like a piece of bleached cardboard.

'Oh, this is terrible my child, say ten Our Fathers and five Hail Mary's and try very hard never to think these bad thoughts again.'

A giggle starts to bubble up inside my chest, reaches my throat and threatens to erupt into my mouth and out into the hallowed air of the front room.

'Are you listening?' I jump. I always jump when my mother raises her voice but the timing was fortuitous, thereby saving me from a severe lecture regarding my deficiency as a human being.

'We went on the train to Leeds, that's where you were born, and fetched you from the house where your real mother was staying. Not a particularly nice district as I recall.' My mother's nose wrinkled in distaste, then she continued. 'No, not at all the kind of place you would want to live. We'd been thinking about adopting a baby for a while, and our Ann kept going on and on about us having another baby. It was fortunate for you that we did because you would have been put into a home.'

For the first time, Ann spoke. 'I was so excited, I could hardly wait for them to bring you back. You were a lovely baby and so tiny.'

I looked at Ann, grateful for her interjection but unable to respond. I was having difficulty understanding who I was. I had a twin sister who I wasn't allowed to see because she was bad, and my past was buried in a grimy district in Leeds, never to re-surface.

* * *

The complexity of this revelation, juxtaposed as it was with what was a difficult childhood, became for me an intangible something which at times I thought about incessantly and at others, disregarded. It wasn't finding out that I had been adopted, I was pleased; it explained why I was different. No, it was the duplicity of everyone else knowing I had a twin sister and most importantly, the disappointment in not knowing who she was and being unable to judge for myself if she was bad. If *she* was wicked then surely I must be? Certainly, during the years which followed as I grew up, I was reminded repeatedly that this in fact was the case. "Bad blood will out" and "you'll end up a slut, like your real mother" were phrases I attempted to immune myself from, unsuccessfully.

My problematic childhood stemmed partly from the fact that I was a difficult child – trouble had a habit of finding me no matter how hard I tried to evade it. I did stupid things which were bound to end in disaster. In the summer, my friend and I would take melted tar from the roadside as we walked home from school and used it like plasticine. Once, I put this into the pocket of my home-made school dress and promptly forgot about it; that is until I arrived home from school finding my mother brandishing a ruined iron. Another time, during dinner, my mother insisted I have a second helping of semolina; which I hated. Just as she was pouring it out, the pan suspended in mid-air, I moved my bowl and the semolina flowed surreally into a heap onto the table cloth, looking remarkably like a terrified pink jelly fish. After twenty minutes of being shouted at loudly, I was banished to the bedroom.

The bedroom which I shared with Ann was in itself fairly uninteresting, the smallness of the room accommodated only a double bed, a wardrobe and a dressing table. However, my sister's possessions were fascinating, particularly her brightly coloured nail varnish. I only wanted to look inside, but as I held the brush and wondered at the shiny, satin sheen of its contents, it dripped like a tear-drop onto the dressing table, where, unlike the semolina, it resembled a jewel lying in languorous splendour against the dark mahogany wood. Feverishly, I tried to remove it by mopping it up with nail varnish remover, the disastrous results of which need only imagination. Thinking on my feet, I placed a dressing table cover over the stain and tried to lie my way out of trouble.

'I didn't do it.'

'Don't you lie to me, who else could have done it?'

Who else indeed? I wasn't even good at lying.

Soon after being told about Elaine, I managed to talk to Ann one night while she was getting ready to go out. I bombarded her with questions I hadn't dared to ask my parents.

'Did you ever see Elaine?' I asked, sitting on the bed watching her tie her hair up in a pony tail.

'Oh yes, we saw her at the Court, when you were legally adopted,' she turned away from the mirror to look at me. 'Your real mother was there too. You look a lot like her.'

'Do I?' I felt quite excited by this news.

'Yes, she had long dark hair in a pageboy style, and very dark eyes. I remember thinking that she must only have been about eighteen or nineteen, but I don't know.' She stopped speaking whilst she applied her lipstick. She never wore much make-up, I didn't find out until many years later that only lipstick was allowed in our house, consequently, the one she wore was a very bright red.

'Did Elaine look like me as well?'

Ann smiled broadly, 'Of course she did, you're twins. Mind, she was bigger than you, I think mam said you were only four pounds when you were born but Elaine was five pounds.'

'I wish I could see her.' I said wistfully.

'What's the matter, am I not a good enough sister for you then?' Ann said, laughing. I immediately felt guilty; Ann was a good sister and very kind hearted.

'No, I didn't mean that, I just meant...'

'It's all right, I know what you meant.' She looked more serious. 'Perhaps it's for the best you don't see her, because she's bound to be different. I know you look alike, but she will behave differently and perhaps you wouldn't like her.'

I stared at Ann in consternation. 'So you think she's bad as well?'

'I'm not saying she is bad, just that she's being brought up differently, so maybe you wouldn't enjoy playing with her.' Ann finished lamely, probably wishing I would disappear.

Standing, she said, 'I think Mr. Logan, Elaine's dad, knew your real mother and that's how they knew you needed a home, but to be honest I don't know them.'

Ann reached for her coat, preparing to leave the room.

'Do you know what my name was before... before I came here?' I asked quickly.

'Sorry love, I don't know that either. But never mind, you're our Mary now, so none of that matters anymore does it?'

'No, I suppose not.'

Chapter Three

My nose pressed tightly against the pet shop window, I watched excitedly the antics of the little marmoset monkey sitting in its cage. This shopping area was called *The Shambles* and comprised of narrow cobbled-stone alley ways. At their apex the buildings leaned toward one other, as if for comfort. The whole locale crouched in the shadow of the Crooked Spire. It was a land mark as well known to the inhabitants of the historic market town of Chesterfield, as their own front doors. Legendary folklore told tales of the Devil wrapping his tale around the steeple in a fit of anger. A less mythical reason was because it had originally been built with green timbers, which warped over time, thus causing the crooked spectacle.

'Do you think Santa would bring me a monkey for Christmas?' I asked.

My father looked down at me, a harassed look on his face.

'Well lass, I don't think it would be very suitable to have in the house, do you?'

'Yes they are Daddy, because a lady brings one to church with her and she dresses it in proper clothes and everything.'

'I wouldn't get your hopes up, I don't think your mam could cope with having a monkey about the place.' He said, looking even more worried than normal.

But my rose-coloured dreams were not easily deterred. 'I heard the lady saying how mischievous her monkey is; he climbed onto her dressing table and put face powder all over himself, but she did say he was usually very good.' I amended swiftly, seeing the look of consternation on my father's face.

'Well, Christmas is a long way off, you might have changed your mind by then.'

'I won't, really, I won't.'

I convinced myself Santa wouldn't ignore my heartfelt pleas, but he did.

Lost in self-pity I was totally unaware that an identical face had pressed against the same window with the same animated excitement, and the same disappointing conclusion.

* * *

As my childhood advanced into double figures my intrinsic strong character began to emerge. I had no idea from whom I had inherited it, but even though my mother was determined to keep the lid tightly fastened, sometimes it would spill out. Not in a whoosh-like steam from a boiling kettle, more like a puff of smoke from a chimney which dissipates on contact with a blast of cold air. Ann's unassuming nature and acceptance of her fate often made me angry on her behalf and would lead to further controversy with my mother. She said I was head-strong, whatever that meant.

One Saturday morning in November not long before our birthdays, when Ann had finished her chores, my mother stood at the top of the stairs like Boudicca addressing her army.

'Do you call this clean? There's still bits of cotton on this carpet, and try using some elbow grease for a change; it looks as if you've never touched this banister, let alone polished it.'

Ann sighed, retrieved the brush and dusters and disappeared through the door without a word. I was sat on the floor beside a small cupboard next to the fireplace trying to find my favourite book, *Jack Joins the Circus.* I picked up a large doll that had seen better days. Her name was Gwyneth, a Celtic name I had chosen on account of numerous holidays spent in Wales. When she arrived, via Father Christmas, her ebony curls bounced around her head like inky corkscrews. Later on her hair began to fall out in great clumps and suddenly she totally disappeared. I searched everywhere, but to no avail. One day a few weeks before Christmas I found her behind my parents' dressing table, her totally bald head covered in a brown glutinous substance, her eye's gleaming with distressed surprise at the indignity. On Christmas morning she reappeared wearing a halo of blonde curls which didn't suit her Celtic nature at all, and she wore a permanent look of shock. I complied with what was expected of me and pretended it was a completely new doll. Now, as I surveyed the grubby blonde locks and time-scarred face, the shocked look seemed to have turned to despairing acceptance and I felt a kinship with her.

My mother came through and sat down in her green fireside chair with wooden arms.

'Haven't you finished tidying that cupboard yet?' Her tone wasn't exactly what you would call kindly, but more conciliatory than usual.

'I was just sorting out the books,' I replied.

My mother lit a cigarette. 'Yes, well make sure you do it properly. I don't know what's got into our Ann, her work's getting very shoddy.' She paused to puff on her cigarette before she went on. 'If you ask me her head's too full of boys, it's time she thought about something else. Your dad works hard to provide a nice house for you two and I won't have her spoiling it. If she doesn't look to her laurels she won't be going to any dance tonight.'

'Oh no, she's been looking forward to it for ages.' The words tumbled out in a rush with no thought to the consequences. Ann had confided in me about Mike, who she was meeting at the dance. They had dated for a while previously but the relationship had foundered. Now though they had started to see each other again.

My mother's attitude towards me changed in an instant.

'And what's it got to do with you madam? Don't you forget you're not twelve years old yet, I won't have you answering me back, particularly about something you know nothing whatsoever about.'

My chin came up and from my position on the floor I looked into her pale, blue eyes. 'Yes, but it's not fair...'

'Don't you "but" me, and I'll tell you what's fair; if she doesn't do her work properly, she's not going and that's my final word on the subject.' Nevertheless, she continued. 'I'll be damned if I'm going to sit here arguing with you about it, you're just a child so mind your own business and get on with cleaning that cupboard.' She stared pointedly at the conglomeration of books and crayons littering the floor. 'And, make sure you do it properly.'

To my shame, I quailed under her gaze, wanting desperately to make life better for Ann, but lacking the temerity needed to withstand my mother's onslaught. I was mortified.

* * *

I liked school. Sometimes I thought it was my saviour, not a saviour in the religious sense, albeit religious enlightenment accompanied my every step. Mass every morning – during which I usually fainted – martyrs, catechisms, confessions, communion, acts of contrition, priests, nuns, rosary beads, and prayer books. No, school was my saviour from home. It wasn't that my academic light shone very brightly, or that I evaded trouble there, although talking was my only disgrace, for which I was frequently caned. Therefore, the only explanation I can offer is that school was reassuringly rigid, where everyone was treated the same and there was no lingering atmosphere of dread. Whatever the reason, I preferred school and begged to go even if my mother occasionally thought I was too ill.

One morning during playtime a girl from another class, whom I knew vaguely, ran by me and then stopped and retraced her steps.

'My sister saw you going into Jimmies,' she said, eyeing me with scorn. 'My sister said she wouldn't be seen dead in that place,' she finished spitefully, before running off to rejoin her friends.

I stared after her with uncomprehending eyes. What was she talking about? Jimmies was a dance-hall in town with a notorious reputation and the nearest I had ever been to a dance hall was the Friday night social held in the church hall, which I attended with my parents. I didn't know where Jimmies was, and wouldn't have been allowed to go even if I had done. Suddenly, a realisation came over me and I raced over to the girl.

'It wasn't me.' I managed breathlessly.

'My sister doesn't lie, who else could it have been?' She asked, her tone laden with irony.

'I think it could have been my twin sister, Elaine.'

I could tell by the way she looked at me that she didn't believe me, so I carried on. 'I've got a twin sister who I don't know, so if the girl your sister saw looked liked me, then it was probably her.'

'Right, okay if you say so.' I could tell she still thought I was lying. 'Still I wouldn't like to think that my sister went to *that* place.' She finished smugly.

I began to worry and fret. For almost four years I had held my twin sister in my head like a beacon of light, albeit a light which had to be hidden from view, but nonetheless a special someone whom I hoped might one day come into my life. The rigid, moral indoctrination within me conjectured that my mother's prediction about Elaine ending up a "bad lot" was right. But nibbling at the edges of my ethical conscience was a longing to be her, to do the things she did. It sounded much more exciting than the Friday night social though anything was more exciting than the Friday night social.

Chapter Four

I ran down the road scrubbing my eyelids with a handkerchief trying to remove blue eye shadow and Cherry-Blossom shoe polish, which substituted for mascara. I had applied this concoction to my eyes at the dance-hall earlier, because even at eighteen, I was absolutely forbidden to wear make-up. I'd missed the 10.30pm bus and was aware that trouble waited, in the form of my mother. She would be sat in her chair facing the door, a cigarette jammed in the corner of her mouth; the smoke curling upwards causing her to squint devilishly. Even so, this was not my prime consideration as I hurried along. At the dance hall a girl had approached me and announced that she knew my twin sister Elaine, and could even tell me whereabouts she worked. I'd carefully written it down, The Adelphi Theatre, London, and hidden it in the furthest reaches of my handbag.

This previously unknown fact made her seem more remote than ever. In my narrow provincial world, the furthest I had travelled from the historic Derbyshire town in which we lived, was to Wales – and London may as well have been on the moon. As a child I'd associated London with the queen; as a teenager with outrageous fashions and even more outrageous pop-stars. I daydreamed that Elvis or Billy Fury would surely fall madly in love with me if only we could meet accidentally. My mother thought they should all be locked up and the key thrown away. To suddenly learn that Elaine was in London, participating in a culture which was as alien to me as a subversive Andy Warhol painting, was on the one hand a bitter blow, but on the other strangely enticing.

I opened the door stealthily.

'And what time do you call this?'

Even though I was expecting it I still jumped. 'I missed the bus. I think it must have gone a few minutes early.' My lame excuse trailed into the air joining forces with the cloud of cigarette smoke, hovering above the black-leaded fireplace.

'More like you were too late again, how many times do I have to tell you? If you don't get home when I say, then you can forget about going out. In fact, I wouldn't have let you go at all if I'd known you hadn't finished that pile of ironing.

'Sorry.'

Yes, well sorry doesn't make it right.' Suddenly she stared hard at me, 'You've got that muck on your face again.' Her voice had turned steely and my stomach turned to jelly.

'No, no I haven't.'

Her invective gathered momentum.

'Don't you lie to me young lady, as if it wasn't bad enough that I have to sit here waiting until you deign to come home, you wilfully disobey me into the bargain. Well, your father will have something to say about this when he finds out you've been out clarted with muck and looking like a tart.' She stopped and eyed me with disgust. 'I suppose you think you'll pull the wool over his eyes, but I know you better; you think you're so clever but you'll end up a slut like your real mother, you mark my words.'

Somehow, this didn't seem like the ideal time to mention Elaine.

* * *

The piece of paper began to fray at the edges as I continuously pulled it from my bag, pondered over it and hastily stuffed it back when I heard someone climbing the stairs. The piece of paper was unneeded because the details were etched on my brain; what I did need was someone to talk to. There was no one I could turn to for advice. Ann would have told me, as she had long ago, to forget about Elaine; but the last thing I wanted to do was forget. Yet I was afraid to write to her because I could envisage the bittersweet outcome. The scenarios were many and varied: there would be a joyful, if tearful, reunion, but my life would not be worth living as my mother would think me ungrateful and harangue me for disobeying her, hadn't she always told me that I wasn't to see Elaine? Even my father may not forgive me for disregarding their wishes. I shredded the problem to pieces in my head until it resembled the tattered piece of paper. The one thing which stopped me was Elaine's reaction when faced with my mother's wrath. My cheeks burned with embarrassment just contemplating it. What would Elaine think? It might result in her never wanting to have anything to do with me again; so I convinced myself it would be better to wait.

So I waited and I waited, and while I waited I fell in love. Throughout my teens I had regularly fallen in and out of love; but Tony was different. He was my soulmate, we could talk about anything and frequently did for long hours. He was tall, with a rugged air which belied his considerate and sensitive nature. He worried about me when he wasn't with me and made me laugh when he was. Because he was in the Royal Navy and based in Portsmouth, our time spent together was often snatched; but always fun. We became engaged on my twentieth birthday.

Despite not contacting Elaine, conditions at home worsened. My mother disliked Tony, his family, my engagement ring and, when sadly my father died after a severe stroke, I was convinced she hated me as well. I felt that not only had I lost a wonderful father, but also a great friend and I missed him terribly. With just the two of us in the house and Tony away at sea for weeks or even months at a time, we should have enjoyed a closeness cemented by the common link of grief, but unfortunately this was not the case. We had a sort of uneasy truce which lasted until Tony was told he was to join *H.M.S. Manxman* in Singapore for a period of two years. But, and this was the good news, if we were to be married before he went, six months earlier than we had planned, I could accompany him. We were euphoric. A new life in a new country – what an opportunity! However, as night follows day, good news is inevitably followed by bad. When I tentatively explained the situation to my mother, the truce collapsed with a vengeance and the atmosphere in the house became intolerable.

'I can't believe I'm hearing this. You mean to tell me that you're planning to leave me here, all on my own?'

She pulled a handkerchief from her pinafore pocket and dabbed at her eyes vigorously. 'Thank God your father's not alive, it would kill him.'

'But, we thought,' I began, trying not to provoke her. 'We thought you might be pleased for us, it's such a great opportunity and the alternative would be spending two years apart.'

'You thought, you thought? Yes, well you obviously didn't once consider my feelings while you were making your fancy plans, did you?'

No I suppose we didn't. Actually, that wasn't strictly true. I had thought about my mother, but only in the form of a paralysing dread when contemplating her reaction. A realisation came over me that perhaps it was unfair; after all it was barely four months since dad had died.

'No, I'm sorry we probably didn't, I think we were so excited about it and I didn't think you would mind too much, me not being here, I mean...' my voice trailed away.

'Well I do mind.'

A dense silence enveloped the room. Whilst I struggled for the right words, my mother stared stonily out of the window with watery eyes. Suddenly she spoke again.

'Anyway, why can't you get married and he can go on his own to Timbuktu or wherever it is?'

'But, we'd have to spend two years apart and...' I stopped. We were both adults, albeit she still thought of me as a child, but why couldn't we have a civilised discussion about this? I took a deep breath.

'You know if this had happened when you and dad were planning to get married, wouldn't you have wanted to go with him?' I asked evenly.

'It didn't, so what's the point of discussing ifs and ands?' She replied tartly.

'Yes, but what if it had, what decision would you have made?' I persisted.

She pinned me with a withering stare. 'I've just told you, it didn't, so it's not an issue.' She paused and sniffed loudly. 'I might have known you'd argue the toss and just because your poor dad isn't here, you think you can browbeat me. Don't you think you've caused enough trouble? It's probably thanks to you and all the worry you caused that he went to an early grave.'

I was used to being the black sheep, but this? I blinked tears from my eyes; she wouldn't see me cry. Over the years it had become a mantra ringing in my head. *Don't let her see you cry. Don't cry, don't cry, don't cry.*

Chapter Five

As the critical moment elongated into minutes, the tears remained unshed, ready to fall later. Briefly, I was reminded of another crucial conversation, many years ago, when I'd been told about being adopted and having a twin sister. Back then, in the front room, I'd had little participation in the discussion and had to comply with their wishes. Now, I was twenty years old and I still didn't have the fortitude to try and contact my own twin sister. I pushed it from my mind; we were in the back room and it wasn't a conversation, it had all the hallmarks of a battlefield. I could even visualise an imaginary demarcation line on the linoleum.

I used to think she couldn't hurt me any more, but to blame me for my father's death shook me more than anything else she had ever accused me of. Swallowing angry retorts, and my pride I said.

'So you won't allow me to go?'

'Since when did anything I say stop you from doing what you want? You please yourself, you always do. Don't you worry about how I'll manage without the extra money, as well as having to live on my own.'

Money had never been an issue in my life, aside from not having any. Since starting work at the Co-operative Insurance Company at the age of fifteen, my mother had taken all my wages, bought my clothes and allotted me spending money. That is, until fairly recently when she acquiesced to my engaged status and allowed me to keep my wages and pay board. This apparently was because I would need the money to pay for the wedding. By this juncture I was earning seven pounds, one shilling per week of which I gave my mother four pounds, ten shillings a week, board. Consequently, I didn't think the deficit would make too much difference; especially as I wasn't living in the house she wouldn't have to buy extra food. I might have been on the skinny side but I had a good appetite. And I considered it an impossibility that she might actually miss me personally; perhaps I'd misjudged her?

An uncomfortable quietness permeated the room, interrupted only by hot coals groaning in indignation as they burnt down to a grey ash. I had to say something, but what? 'I'm going whatever you say.' Or, 'All right, you've won the battle. I won't go.' My heart twisted at the thought of two years apart from Tony; it seemed like a lifetime. The thought of a new life on the other side of the world filled me with an elation I hadn't felt before. I longed for a life that wouldn't be compromised by my mother's whims. Constantly observing how Ann's marriage to Mike was rocked by my mother's interference, I didn't want my marriage meandering down a road strewn with sharp pebbles. Still, despite my mother's outrageous accusation, was I lacking in moral sensibility? Perhaps I was selfish and thinking only of my own happiness.

'Maybe we should both think about it some more.' I ventured.

She looked at me but stayed silent.

I was becoming desperate. 'Obviously, it will take some getting used to, but I'll be getting married next year so I'll be leaving then anyway.'

'I don't see why you can't live here, there's two bedrooms, or you could buy that house in the next street that's for sale.'

Although her words seemed innocuous, they filled me with dread. If we lived in this house I may as well sign the divorce papers now, before the wedding. She had already tried to split us up; telling Tony that I'd gone out with another boy whilst he was away. She didn't succeed even though it was true; I had already told him before we got engaged. Living in the next street would be little better, even Ann lived two bus rides away. As for buying a house, we could barely afford the wedding, let alone buy property.

'That would nice, but we couldn't possibly afford to buy a house.' I sounded like a sickly cat begging for its tenth life so I hurried on before I lost courage. 'Even if we did live here, I'd still like to go to Singapore with Tony.' I paused, trying to communicate my innermost feelings. 'Being apart for two years would be so awful, I don't know if...'

'For goodness sake stop being so melodramatic,' she interrupted. 'You'll still be married. Your problem is that you want everything, well you'll learn that in this life you can't always have it.'

The battle sunk without trace into the muddied trench inside my head. Opting for cowardice I said.

'Honestly I really don't want to argue. Can we think about it and talk again tomorrow?' Delivering this pathetic volley I turned to open the door of the front room to go to bed.

'Yes, go on, you walk away then you won't have to worry your head about me.'

Her voice cut sharply through the air and rang in my ears as I climbed the stairs.

* * *

A heavy weight settled on me at work the next day. Tony would be coming home at the weekend and I didn't have any answers. Maybe it was wrong, but I found myself pouring my heart out to the girls I worked with. There were twelve of us in the office: two managers, three typewriters, one, very old adding machine, jealously guarded by the Chief Clerk, and thirty-six insurance agents who visited en masse every two weeks for their accounts to be audited.

What surprised me most of all was their reaction to my news; they were delighted, thought it was a wonderful opportunity and couldn't understand my problem. I explained briefly about my mother's objections.

'Have you talked it over with her?' Anne asked, a girl already married and one of the kindest people I knew.

'Yes, I tried last night, but she's adamant. I really want to go, but I feel I'm being really selfish. Apart from which, she probably won't allow me to.'

'If you ask me, it's her who is being selfish. I know my mother would be thrilled if I was able to do something like that.' She looked up from the claim form she was working on. 'Fat chance of that happening,' she laughed. 'Obviously it's your decision, I can only say what I would do and I'd definitely be going. And, by the way, your mother can't stop you, don't forget you'll be twenty-one in a few weeks.'

'What difference will that make?' I asked.

'Twenty-one is the legal age of consent, so as long as you get married after your birthday you won't need her permission to either get married or leave and go to Singapore, so I would think carefully about it before you decide.'

Some of the other girls agreed with Anne and my spirits lightened, not much but it helped me to put the dilemma into its proper prospective. Carolyn, another friend whom I'd worked with for a few years and knew about Elaine, asked me if I had ever tried to contact her?

I shook my head sadly. 'No I haven't, but I wish I had.'

This latest development in my life had almost obliterated Elaine from my head, and as I thought about it now, I despondently wondered if perhaps it was never meant to be. Did she still work at the Adelphi Theatre? Did she still live in London? I sighed, wishing on the one hand that I had written to her, and then, on the other that it would just be another

45

complication I couldn't cope with. It appeared I was destined to go through life making ineffectual decisions.

* * *

Looking wonderful in his naval uniform, Tony asked, 'Did your mother agree?'

Alcohol was not permitted in our local dance-hall "The Vic", so we sat on the balcony partaking of a soft drink.

I looked at him wryly. 'What do you think?'

I filled him in on what had occurred and he looked suitably gloomy, being no stranger to my mother's abrasive tongue.

'What shall we do?' I said.

'Darling, to get away and live a life of our own without all the traumas is the one thing I want most in the world, but ultimately it's got to be your decision. I don't want you to do anything which will make you unhappy, but...' he paused. 'Oh, lets just do it and to hell with the consequences. I can't bear to leave you for two years, and knowing how she'll treat you will make it twice as hard.'

We were both silent for long minutes. Then he said, 'We've got to make a decision, because if we are going together, I've got to arrange the married-accompanied paper work as soon as I get back to the ship.'

"There's a place for us" P.J. Proby sang in his deep vibrant voice.

Tony looked at me and took my hand in his. There was a place for us; and it wasn't here.

* * *

The decision made, I actually told my mother, surprising even myself. I didn't beg or plead or offer platitudes. We were in the front room, the geese still in position on the wall; but now their suicide mission had been aborted and they appeared to know exactly where they were going. Suddenly, I'd grown up and I think she realised it. Nevertheless, she didn't take it well. Eventually, she conceded that I could go, but insisted that I couldn't fly out with Tony on the 19th January. I was to stay behind with her for three months to give her time to get used to the idea. I acquiesced immediately. What was three months compared to the rest of our lives? Fortunately, Tony was able to rearrange my flight date and conscientiously we began to organise our wedding for the 7th January, which would give us just twelve days together before he flew to Singapore.

My birth certificate seemed non-existent. I'd never seen one and previously never needed one; but now I did. As the appointment date with the Registrar loomed closer, I reverted to my usual mass of nerves, wondering how I could broach the subject without causing too much collateral damage. To my astonishment, my mother came downstairs one evening and handed me an old, but important looking document.

'I've looked this out for you, I thought you might be needing it,' she said.

It was my adoption papers. Grateful that I hadn't had to ask her for the documentation, kind thoughts kindled within me; everything was going to be all right. Maybe she cared after all and had accepted my forthcoming marriage. It was, I thought, an olive branch, and clasping both the metaphorical branch and the tangible document with both hands, I thanked her warmly.

I inspected the document closely and there it was; my original name. Diane Cohen. Initially registered in the district of Blenheim, Leeds, England. I had been taken to court at Chesterfield on the 23rd April 1946 and legally adopted by Doris and James Black, and Leah Cohen, my own birth mother, had attended.

I said the name over and over in my head, Diane Cohen. I felt suited to the name, felt it to be more part of my persona than the name I had. Perhaps it was only because this epithet had been an enigma to me for thirteen years. The stark, black printing outweighed the fantasy I had woven around who I really was. Now it had substance and I liked it. Feeling happy, I was totally unaware how my present circumstances would preclude the chance of being reunited with my twin sister.

Chapter Six

Our wedding took place on the 7th January 1967, despite everything conspiring to spoil it. The day did not dawn bright, it was black. Dense fog blanketed the earth, attempting to disguise the sleet and snow which fell lethargically from a leaden sky. My mother, who had barely spoken to me over the previous week, other than to inform me I was not to have a baby whilst living abroad, was adamant that she would not come to our wedding; then changed her mind the day before. We had had to invite people we barely knew and couldn't afford to pay for. With seven shillings and sixpence between us, we boarded a train for Sheffield, ten miles away, for our two night honeymoon. In spite of the adversity, in spite of the weather, in spite of having little money, we were ecstatic and went out for a meal and ate bread sticks for the first time, feeling frivolous and free.

Even when Tony left me twelve days later, I walked around in a suppressed state of jubilation, constantly looking forward to April when I would join him. My emotions might have been different if I'd known the last words my mother uttered to Tony before he left the house; something he did not tell me until many years later.

* * *

Ann's eyes filled with tears as we said goodbye. It was a poignant moment leaving her but even so, I couldn't wait to join

Tony and begin my new life as a new bride in a foreign country. I felt caught up in a vortex of anticipation which gripped me in a feverish cloak of excitement.

Notwithstanding that I had only once travelled alone on a train, I took to flying like a newly hatched butterfly. It was night when we landed in Kuwait to refuel and the airport looked like a glorified hut in the middle of an infinite desert. My imagination, which hadn't diminished with the years, worked overtime. We were greeted by a dark, solemn-faced man swathed from head to toe in flowing robes, between the folds of which hung a long sword glinting in the moonlight. This was definitely more exciting than falling from my tricycle. Our second re-fuelling stop was Ceylon – now Sri Lanka. The sun glinted off a cerulean ocean, garlanded by an arc of incredibly white sand. Leaving this picturesque scene behind, the plane climbed high into the sky and was immediately buffeted by an electric storm. I was surrounded by the sound of crying babies and people vomiting. Unperturbed, I munched on the fresh pineapple we had been served and surveyed the ever-changing earth beneath us, thinking about Tony who would meet me in Singapore and thinking about the twin sister I had never known.

* * *

Our new address, 12, Jalan Perwira, Johore Bahru, Malaya, a semi-detached bungalow, was situated over the causeway from Singapore. Albeit, Jalan is a mundane word meaning road, but Perwira translated as unknown and I found our new address as mesmerising as the country. The jungle sprawled beyond our back door, its mysterious interior appearing like forbidden territory. But a closer inspection would sometimes reveal nothing more sinister than old rubber flip-flops which were produced in a ramshackle factory a few hundred metres away. Tropical rain pounded the canopy everyday at precisely one o'clock, shrouding the surrounding landscape in a metallic curtain. Encapsulated within this hot and humid terrain lived a multi-cultural society who were an amalgam of the weird, the wonderful, and the whimsical.

Most days an emaciated sacred cow with a mournful face would amble by our wrought-iron gates searching for a blade of grass which hadn't been scorched to oblivion by the sun. Meanwhile, its owner, an Indian gentleman, sporting an equally mournful expression, lounged on the ground shaking his head dolefully. The Chinese "blue egg man" so called because he rode a rickety, old blue bicycle, fired conversation at the Cantonese Amah like a sub-machine gun, and I was convinced he was summoning up the Terracotta Army. But my favourite local visitor was the Malayan Insurance man. He wore a horrible brown suit and diligently mopped his shiny face with a handkerchief of the same dun colour; whilst cheerfully informing us that for "a few bobs a week" we could live like kings when we were dead.

Our own culture was very different from the colourful inhabitants, but we respected their customs and fitted in well. Although our diet comprised mainly of the English food we could obtain, we also incorporated local dishes into our eating habits and Tony would fetch succulent prawns from the cold-storage – the equivalent of our English village shop. He was also given to picking up Satay – a Malay Pork skewer – from the man who sat on the ground at the top of the road with his charcoal brazier. When the meat ran out he would douse the flames and hoist the whole contraption over his shoulder and presumably head for home. I couldn't bring myself to partake in this travelling cuisine, notwithstanding the lack of hygiene, surely in one hundred and twenty degrees Fahrenheit, the pork must have been rancid?

Another local delicacy neither of us could face, were the tiny silver coloured dried fish, which inevitably graced the tables at Chinese mealtimes. In Singapore City and Jahore Bahru, the obnoxious smell emanating from the dried fish stalls attacked our nostrils from thirty metres away. The stalls resembled rivers of silver moonbeams, but the stench eradicated the illusion and we would run the gauntlet of odour, holding our noses.

I had gone from being treated like a servant, to having one of my own. The Royal Navy decreed that British girls were too delicate to undertake their own chores in the energy sapping heat, so paid the sailors enough money to employ an Amah. Three days a week a Chinese Amah called Kim, who spoke very little English, would enter our home. I never got used to the idea. Prior to her arrival I would rise early, make sure all the dishes were washed, and the place spotless. One morning, running late, I was still in the throes of my pre-servant clean-up.

'Missy no wash dishes.' She said, vigorously shaking her head.

'Oh, it's all right Kim, I don't mind,' I said, smiling.

'No, no, not right Missy, Kim do.' Her voice had gone up two octaves in her agitation as she bustled towards the sink, which intimated it was her domain and not mine. I backed away from the kitchen; perhaps she thought I didn't want to employ her. Kim's mother worked for our friends, Rosemary and Alan, who lived next door, and I had visions of her running in tears to her mother saying I didn't need her. It was a very perplexing time and a huge learning curve about the culture of another country that isn't one's own.

Regardless of the humidity, cockroaches, lizards eating crumbs off the carpet, poisonous snakes, bats flying inadvertently into the lounge, I never once thought I would prefer to be back in England. Despite previously being frightened by the tiniest moth, I coped quite well; until one night when I visited Rosemary next door. Tony and her husband, Alan, were away at sea, and she had just put her two children to bed. Suddenly a macabre scream almost sent me spiralling onto the ceiling alongside the whirring fan.

'Oh my gawd.' Rosemary's inherent cockney accent became more pronounced when she became agitated.

'What is it?' I asked fearfully.

With eyes as big as saucers, she pointed mutely to the wall. My eyes followed her stricken gaze where a spider the size of a dinner plate had ensconced itself on the wall and was peering regally at its pathetic subjects. I ran to her side, for protection. Rosemary was normally capable of dealing with anything that life threw at her, but spiders were not on her list of things to be dealt with firmly. The thick hairs which covered the spider's body and legs, glowed a magnificent shade of mahogany and commanded our undivided attention. Suddenly, it began to wave two long hairy legs in the air as if conducting an orchestra. Like a responsive audience we stood rooted to the spot and watched in awe.

'What are we going to do?' Rosemary croaked.

'I don't know,' I managed to whisper.

Suddenly it ran with alarming speed across the wall and settled itself sedately above Rosemary's sleeping baby's door.

'Oh no,' she wailed. 'I can't leave Jaqui in there with that thing. What if it goes in?'

'I know there are gaps above the door Rosemary, but it's so big I doubt it could get through.' I replied, trying to placate her.

She ran an elegant hand through her blonde hair. 'I know, why don't you fetch Tops?'

'What for?' I asked curiously. Tops was our dog, albeit an excellent guard dog but a stupid mutt nonetheless.

'To catch the bloody thing of course,' she replied.

'Oh, right,' I said, doubtfully. I knew for a fact he couldn't even catch his own tail.

But I was proved wrong. After twenty minutes of sustained encouragement from both Rosemary and myself, much excited barking and panting, he finally cornered it, grabbed it in his mouth and stood wagging his tail, while long hairy legs thrashed about his face.

'Take it outside Tops.' His tail wagged furiously.

'TAKE IT OUT!'

Eventually, he got the message and trotted proudly into the night with his catch.

Rosemary was so overcome by his bravery that she fed him chocolates for the remainder of the evening.

The next day I received a letter from England which contained information that eclipsed the escapade with the harmless fruit spider.

Chapter Seven

The letter sat on the table looking as innocuous as a dead wasp, but the sting was far from harmless. I re-read the pertinent paragraph again and again, as if by some miracle the contents would change.

I took a phone call at work last week, you'll never guess who it was? Your twin sister, Elaine! Apparently she'd come up from London especially to find you and was so pleased to have discovered where you worked. You can imagine how disappointed she was when I told her you had got married and gone to live in Singapore three months ago. Honestly Mary, I was so surprised by the call it wasn't until later I realised that I hadn't given her your address. I'm so sorry.

I couldn't blame Carolyn. She wasn't to know how important it was to me. No, it was my own fault for being weak and scared; I should have contacted Elaine when I had the chance, now it was too late. I walked outside into the garden with the letter still in my hand. The humid heat wrapped around my body as if to cocoon me from the hurt. I felt as if I had let Elaine down; I wasn't there when she came for me and it seemed somehow that fate had betrayed us and we were destined never to meet. I sensed a loss of my identity and watched it disappear over the horizon. Would I ever be found? The previously joyful sky became sullen and huge spots of rain splattered onto the mammoth leaves of the banana tree at the bottom of Rosemary's garden. I felt as if the sky was weeping for us.

* * *

Tony was sympathetic, but pragmatic.

'You weren't to know that Elaine would come to Chesterfield looking for you.'

'Well I should have known,' I said, fatuously. 'If only I'd written to her before... Now, she'll think I'm not interested in meeting her.'

'Well, I wouldn't get too despondent, perhaps it wasn't meant to be,' Tony said.

'Do you think it's fate?' I said, adding before Tony could reply. 'Perhaps we're destined never to meet,' I said glumly.

Tony grinned, 'Fate? More like bad timing. Look, don't go upsetting yourself about something over which you have no control. Maybe in a few years time when we're back in the UK you'll be able to find her yourself.'

I thought about this carefully. Yes, it was true – there would be no one to stop me now I was older, well I didn't think so. In the meantime I had a lot of other things to think about. Despite my mother's pre-wedding warning of "no babies" I was in fact pregnant by design, and on the 6th April 1968 we were blessed with a beautiful baby daughter, whom we called Lisa Maria. She had a full head of black hair, porcelain white skin and, unlike me, a serene nature. I kept her shaded from the searing heat of the sun and people marvelled at the paleness of her skin. She was, and still is, pale and interesting.

Over the two years we were abroad, I wrote letters to Ann and my mother and mailed dozens of photographs. It was easy for me to eulogise over my first-born and I began to think that my mother was pleased she had a granddaughter; Ann had by this time produced three sons. But I was sadly mistaken.

When it was time for us to return to the UK, all our large items, including the cot which was much larger than its English counterpart, had to be transported by ship prior to us returning by air. Who could have imagined that a baby's cot would be the cause of so much trauma?

Although we couldn't be sure how it would work out, Tony and I agreed we would spend equal time with our respective families before moving to Scotland; Tony's next posting. We thought it would be easier for Tony's father to assemble the cot, as my mother was alone, so we shipped it directly to his parents' home address. Consequently, we could spend the first half of Tony's leave with them and transport the cot ourselves to my mother's house, for our visit with her.

When I wrote to my mother to confirm these arrangements, you would have thought we had procured a hit-man who would ensure her slow and tortuous demise. Her reply was terse and to the point. She said she might have known we'd be going to "his side" without a thought that she would want us to stay with her first. But then, why should she be surprised at my "inconsiderate behaviour"? It appeared, despite my faint hope, the two years away had changed nothing. I replied straight away, painstakingly pointing out the logistics of our possessions, which might prove difficult for her and how we could still visit her even whilst staying with Tony's parents, and then we would stay an equal time with her. I rambled on and on, attempting to achieve the impossible, to make things right between us. I had to make her understand that this had not been arranged as a "slight", as she put it. Although I had carefully composed the letter in order not to cause any offence, it was to no avail. Two weeks later we received a letter, actually I doubt such an epithet could be given to the piece of paper inside the envelope. There was no term of address; just a few stark lines.

Don't think you're doing me any favours. I don't want you or that baby coming to my house so you'd better make other arrangements. If you send any correspondence to me in the future, I wish it to be known that you will address me as Mrs. Black. And another thing, when you get back make sure you fetch all the rubbish you left here, I'll be damned if I'll give it house room. And don't go blubbing to our Ann, she has at last seen you for what you are and agrees with me.

Mrs. Doris Black.

How could a flimsy piece of air-mail paper cause such a range of emotions? I felt stunned, bewildered and upset, but by far the most over-riding emotion was anger. The anger permeated my whole being. I can never remember feeling anger like it before, or since. In the past all I had ever felt was fear regarding my mother's tirades, I had appealed, I had appeased and acceded; but this wasn't about me anymore. She had dragged my baby into the parameters of her own odious mind-set in order, it would appear, to bring me back into line, to resume the total domination which seemed to give her such pleasure. By including those two small words "that baby" she had defined my life from thereon in, and despite the guilt that assailed me from time to time over the coming years, I was adamant that our child, or any subsequent children we might have, would never be contaminated by her.

Chapter Eight

A gleam of watery sunlight filtered through battleship grey clouds and bathed the Pentland Hills in a silvery glow. On a clear summer's day the vista from our small first-floor flat was very different. The bright sunlight and gentle breezes would turn the undulating hillside into every shade of green. Sometimes sheep would appear, either singly or in flocks, roaming the hills looking for sweet new grass. It was winter now and skiers would sweep down the artificial ski slope, not visible from our window, whooping with delight. Despite the looming clouds and grey tinged earth, it was still a magnificent view.

The interior of the flat painted a very different picture. A large table squatted on ugly carved legs; at some time in it's murky past it had been painted black, probably to disguise the deep gouges covering the surface. The sickly looking beige settee and two armchairs were worn and one step away from being threadbare. The only form of heating in the flat was a two-bar electric fire in the lounge. In the depth of winter, ice would form on the inside of the windows as well as the outside. You would have thought that after living in the tropics we would have hated it, but we didn't. The Edinburgh people were warm and welcoming and we made lots of friends. Almost one year after arriving in Scotland, I gave birth to a son, Steven Mark, and our sunny, mischievous little boy completed our family unit. Despite Tony's salary being far less than he had received whilst serving in the Far East, we managed. I still followed my religious teachings, attending mass, confession and communion regularly and totally involved myself in the social ethos of the church. Life was good except for one thing. Inside me was a vacuum which seemed unnatural, like an expanse of ocean which had dried up. Sometimes I failed to recognise the reason, but as the years lined up behind me and sank into the setting suns, deep down I knew it was the absence of my twin. Then, a fortuitous twist of fate materialised out of the blue and suddenly the sun shone again.

* * *

At 7.30pm one Tuesday evening in March 1972, Tony was away and the children were sleeping. As I flopped into the worn easy chair to watch the Tom Jones Show, I had no indication how viewing this particular programme would change my life. As the show reached its dying minutes, I felt too tired to get up immediately and start the chores, so I watched idly as the credits rolled. A popular dance troupe, called *The Young Generation* came to the front of the stage to take their applause whilst their names scrolled up the screen.

Vince Logan

It was a momentary glance. Vaguely I saw a young man with blond hair, but the name appeared to jump from the screen into my senses. All trappings of tiredness left me in an instant, Elaine's name was etched on my brain... Elaine Logan... and even though I wasn't certain, I recalled someone telling me she had a brother named Vince. It could have been either of my parents, or my sister Ann. Maybe it was the girl at the dance-hall, who all those years ago had told me Elaine was in London? I couldn't be sure, but I felt convinced it was Elaine's brother. I roamed around the flat, as much as the small space allowed. I put the cat out, then immediately let her in again. She gave me a look of disdain, as only cats are capable of doing, and meowed to go back outside. I wished Tony was here. I couldn't telephone anyone, despite the fact that a black telephone sat in the corner on a shelf. It was useless. Lack of funds meant we'd had to have it disconnected.

Eventually I went to bed, but I couldn't sleep. Should I contact the BBC? Should I try to contact *The Young Generation*? Then I reasoned it might be a coincidence that the dancer was called Vince Logan and just wishful thinking on my part that it was Elaine's brother. Even if it was her brother she may not be interested in being reunited with me. Or, if she was, how would it work out? Perhaps she would be so different that we wouldn't get on. The myriad questions were endless, as was the night.

Chapter Nine

I stood with the door open, both children clinging to my jeans, waving as Tony loped down the road with his distinctive sailor's gait. I felt like jumping up and down in excitement, like the children. We greeted Tony in a flurry of kisses and hugs which always accompanied his homecoming, went inside where the children fell upon the presents that 'daddy' inevitably bought them from his trips away.

'I've been dying for you to come home.'

'Well I'm pleased to hear it,' Tony said wryly.

'No, I'm always pleased silly, I meant I think I might have learned something about Elaine. I was watching the television the other night and I saw the name of a dancer, it was Vince Logan. I'm sure it could be her brother, but then again it might not be. What do you think?' The words fell over each other in my haste to convey this momentous news.

Tony came over to me as I set the hideous table for dinner, and put his arms around me.

'Well as I didn't see it, I don't know yet what I think. What programme were you watching at the time?' He asked patiently.

'It was The Tom Jones Show on the BBC.'

'Well I think you should write to him and find out if it is Elaine's brother,' he said.

'Yes, well I thought that, but then I thought who will I write to? Then I thought what if I do write and it isn't him, I'll feel really stupid.' I was beginning to lose faith in what had seemed like a good idea.

Tony sat down to drink his beer. 'Too many thoughts if you ask me. Why don't you just write and ask him, it doesn't matter if he's not her brother, it's not as if he knows you.'

I mulled this over for a few seconds. 'Okay, but shall I write to the BBC or to *The Young Generation*?' I was being annoyingly persistent, but I needed to get it right.

Tony sighed, probably feeling totally exasperated by me going on and on the minute he walked through the door. 'I would just write to him care-of them both, that way it should reach him one way or the other.'

I smiled. Tony always knew the best course of action, unlike me who was eternally beset with doubts. 'Yes, I'll do it tomorrow,' I said decisively.

* * *

Saying I would do it and actually performing the task were two different things. I sat down with pen and paper and wrote:

Dear Mr. Logan,

For long moments I stared at the characterless putty coloured wallpaper, as if inspiration would leap from its uninteresting face straight onto the blank sheet of writing paper. I wrestled with sentences and immediately disregarded them. Like Dr. Samuel Johnson, I agonised over every word, but with considerably less success than him. No doubt Voltaire's *Men of Letters* would have made short work of it. But not gifted with literary brilliance, I eventually decided on a plain, direct approach.

I am writing to enquire if you have a sister called Elaine Logan? My reason for asking is because I have an identical twin sister whom I've never met, owing to our being adopted into different families when we were babies. We were born in Leeds and adopted into the town of Chesterfield in Derbyshire. I know that she worked in London at the Adelphi Theatre many years ago and I think someone once told me she has a brother called Vince. I saw you on The Tom Jones Show and decided it was worth trying to contact you in the hope that you are, in fact, Elaine's brother.

If you are the person I'm seeking I would be really grateful if you could pass on my name and address to Elaine and ask if she could write to me. If you are not her brother then I apologise for any inconvenience I may have caused you.

Thank you,
Yours sincerely

I put it into the envelope, wrote the somewhat bizarre address... c/o The BBC, c/o The Young Generation, Television House, London... and fell to thinking about the consequences of my actions. On the one hand how would she feel after all these years hearing from me out of the blue? On the other hand she had tried to contact me before when I'd lived in Singapore, so hopefully she wouldn't have changed her mind. Then again, because we were so much older she may dismiss the idea of wanting to know me at all. Then another thought struck me. What if we didn't like each other? What if we had absolutely nothing in common? After all, her life appeared so very different from mine and as far as I knew, which was very little, it may always have been. The 'what ifs' whirled around my brain like a snowstorm in a bottle. Eventually, I stopped dithering and popped the letter into the bright red pillar-box. I had a strong feeling that my destiny lay within the small, insignificant envelope. For better or worse I had done it and there was nothing to be done now, except wait.

Chapter Ten

The following week dragged by in an ecstasy of agony, it was like *Waiting For Godot.*[1] Previously, I'd been unable to envisage anything past the finding. Now my over-active imagination painted many pictures of the long view. Maybe it wasn't Elaine's brother and he wouldn't have time to answer such a bizarre request. If it was, would she write quickly, or would she take time to think about the consequences? Would she write at all? Did she even exist? I gave myself a mental shake. Of course she existed I think I'd believed in her from when I was five years old outside the cinema, because even though I'd first thought the photograph was me; I knew it was Elaine.

As I pushed my way through the throngs of people on Princes Street I was reminded of columns of ants, scurrying through grass, up and down walls and finally into their mountainous home with prey destined for the queen. No obstacle could distract these soldier ants from their task, their dedication was absolute. And so it is with human beings. We scurry about our daily lives, nurturing our dreams and hopes like secret gemstones, always aware that someone could snatch them from us. This was how I felt, optimistic one minute and pessimistic the next. This confused state I found myself in was actually very short, because on the sixth day of waiting I

---

[1] *'Waiting For Godot'* by Samuel Beckett 1954. Revised Edition 1965 Samuel French – London 2004

received a letter. The letter was from Elaine, the address was New Maldon in Surrey.

Dear Mary,

What a wonderful, wonderful surprise. I could hardly believe my eyes when Vince gave me your letter. He came rushing up waving it in the air saying "You'll never guess who this is from sis!" After all the years of wondering where you were and what you were doing... when I tried to find you I was told you had gone to live in Singapore... I really thought we were destined never to meet.

Where to begin? I just want to know everything about you. Are you married? Have you got a family? Are you happy? I know this is silly because it will probably take ages to find out everything and get to know you; after all it's twenty-eight years. I know it sounds strange but because I knew about you from being very small, I almost feel like I know you already. My mum told me I was special because I had twin sister, and do you know I've always felt special. Now I feel... well I can't find a word which describes how I feel. Happy, ecstatic and exhilarated all rolled into one might do the trick. What do you think?

We will have to get together as soon as possible, so we can really get to know each other properly. You didn't put your phone number on your letter or I would have rung you. Can you let me know when you write back?

I groaned inwardly we didn't have a telephone; well not one that we could actually use. But I pushed it from my mind and continued reading, drinking in every word, every comma, every full stop. She had been married for a year, to Christian, who was French and the Assistant Manager at the Café Royale in London. Her name was now Elaine Allin and she was the box office manageress at the Adelphi Theatre in London, which was about to change as she was just pregnant with their first child. Enclosed with the letter was a small photograph of her and Christian on their wedding day.

Some lengthy scrutinising of the photo revealed someone who was me, but wasn't me. She was wearing a Victorian gown complete with large-brimmed matching hat and parasol. She had a Vidal Sassoon bobbed hairstyle and looked like a model for Christian Dior. It was like seeing myself in another dimension. I loved my own wedding dress made from wild silk and guipure lace with corresponding coronet and veil, but I didn't look like a model. Maybe if I'd been allowed to wear make-up I conjectured. No, probably not. Christian had the air of a dark smouldering, Frenchman; so unlike Tony who was blond and rugged. So, our taste in men was very different. Then again, in the circles in which I had moved, nobody was French, or any other nationality. I sat picturing the kind of place they might have met. A chic nightclub? The French Riviera aboard a sleek yacht? Or perhaps Elaine had dined at the Café Royale and Christian had fallen in love with her over a glass of very expensive wine? Her life was so unlike mine, how could I possibly speculate?

Returning to the letter, I read it and re-read it many times. She was right, we needed to talk, to meet, to get to know each other. When this would happen I had no idea. Financially, we could not afford to make the trip from Edinburgh to London, in fact we couldn't afford to take a trip anywhere. We had managed one holiday in a caravan just over the Forth Bridge to a little place in Fife called Largo Bay, but long journeys were out of the question. First though, I would write and tell her that I would telephone her from a phone box.

This was resolved later that day when I was having coffee with Pat, my friend from the flat downstairs, and Helen who lived two doors away. I was bursting with the news about Elaine and they were delighted for me.

'That's wonderful hen. Why don't you give Elaine my phone number and a time to ring you when the children are in bed?' Helen generously offered.

'That would be great Helen, but are you sure Jimmy won't mind?' Jimmy was her husband.

'Och, away with you, of course he won't mind,' she replied, with munificence – a trait I'd found typical in all of my Scottish friends.

'Thanks Helen, if you're sure. I'll write and give Elaine your number. When will it be convenient?'

'Any evening, it won't matter. I'll make sure the children are nay bother, so you can have a good old blether.'

'You could also give her my number as well, just in case she needs to ring at a different time,' Pat said. 'I'm just so thrilled for you dear, in fact I can't wait to hear from her either.' Pat laughed. 'Och will you listen to me, anyone would think it was my twin sister.'

Pat was eleven years older than me and much like an older sister. Which often made up for the silence from Ann. Not always of course; there were times when I felt totally guilt-ridden about her. I knew she wouldn't dare to contact me and probably took my mother's side because intrinsically she was too frightened to do otherwise. Just as I hadn't had the courage to contact Elaine all those years ago. But all that was in the past, and I was on the brink of a whole new chapter in my life. I confess, I never stopped to think at that juncture what it would mean to my family, to Tony, Lisa and Steven. If I had been thinking coherently I would have realised that another me in their lives would be bound to affect them.

A letter to Elaine winged its way back down south the next day, together with a photograph taken on Lisa's first birthday. Although it wasn't up to date – because I always looked terrible on photographs – it was the best one I could find that wouldn't have her questioning our identical status. Having explained our phone situation, I said I hoped she would be able to ring Helen and Jimmy's on Tuesday evening at seven o'clock. The children would be in bed, which Tony and I agreed was best. At two and four years old, they were possibly too young to understand the complexity of the situation. I hoped fervently, they would be meeting their Aunty Elaine in the not too distant future.

Tony was so pleased. He kept hugging me and grinning, saying, 'God, I wonder what it'll be like having two of you around?'

'Don't get carried away; you can't cope with me, let alone another one,' I retorted.

'That's very true. Can you write another letter and tell her you've changed your mind.'

I threw a cushion at him.

Tuesday finally came around. I stood in Helen's hall waiting for the telephone to ring, nerves clustering like limpets in my stomach. It wasn't the ominous knot which had plagued my insides when I was young – it was anticipation, it was the culmination of a dream I'd been waiting for all my life. The shrill bell of the telephone shattered the stillness of the hallway.

Elaine and Christian
April 1970

Mary and Tony Jan1967

Chapter Eleven

I picked the phone up carefully, as if any swift movement might sever the connection. 'Hello.'

'Hello, Mary?'

Two words, the audible anticipation echoing my own.

'Yes, yes it's me, is that Elaine?' I answered a little breathlessly.

'Yes it is, I was sure it was you, but just in case your friend answered I thought I'd better check.' Elaine laughed and as her easy laughter came clearly down the connection, I began to relax.

Did she sound like me? I had no idea at this juncture what my own voice sounded like, awful probably. She spoke with a posh accent. The answer would be no then.

'It's so great to be talking to you, after all these years of wondering what it would be like. But it's fine and now I feel stupid for being so anxious.'

'No, not stupid,' she replied, 'just natural. I was nervous as well, after all it's not every day you speak to a twin sister you've never met. Although I did see you once when we were quite small.'

'Did you? What happened? I don't remember anything about it.' I could hardly contain myself.

'Well you wouldn't. I was with my mum and two brothers and my mum pointed to the other side of the street and explained to me who you were. You were with your mother and I asked if we could go across the road and talk to you. I'd always known about you, probably before I could even speak properly. Mum was a bit upset but said no because your parents wouldn't allow us to have any contact. I was only small and had a big problem understanding why,' Elaine finished.

'How could you understand? I didn't understand either. Even when I was older I didn't dare mention your name in case it caused a furore,' I said.

'How strange, my mum would have loved it if we'd been able to see each other. Listen Mary, there's so much we have to talk about, and Christian and I have discussed it at length, and decided I could come up to see you, probably next month, what do you think?'

I was ecstatic. 'That would be brilliant. I keep thinking about how we could meet, because to be honest Elaine, we couldn't afford to come down to London. Also with Tony being in the Navy he's away at sea quite a lot, as you can imagine,' I finished with a wry laugh.

'Well that's settled then, and if I come before the baby is born, it will be so much easier.'

'Elaine I'm so sorry, I forgot to congratulate you. You must be thrilled,' I replied, feeling guilty because I hadn't remembered immediately.

'Don't worry, in the excitement I almost forgot myself. If you can let me know where to stay, we could then decide on the best date,' Elaine said.

Forgetting the lack of space, putty-coloured walls and worn furniture I straight away said, 'But you must stay with us, that is if you want to?' I added quickly, realising it sounded like an order.

'I'd love to stay with you but will you have enough space?' Elaine queried.

'Well I must confess the flat isn't very big, but Tony's parents and his sister come to stay, and when friends arrive we always manage. Not that you will have to manage, you will be able to have our bedroom.'

'I wouldn't dream of turning you out of your bedroom,' Elaine replied.

'No honestly it will be fine, no problem at all. Besides, the nearest place I could think of for you to stay would be a bus ride away and it wouldn't give us much talking time.' I realised with a start that Elaine and I were talking together as if we had known each other all our lives.

We started to laugh and neither one of us needed to say why.

* * *

Helen and Pat could see by my animated face that all had gone well as I relayed the phone call to them verbatim. On winged feet I rushed back to our flat to tell Tony. He seemed pleased, but somehow not as ecstatic as I thought he should be. However, I dismissed the niggling doubt, after all, why should he feel like me, it wasn't his twin.

The following week I walked around with my head literally in the clouds, bathed in an ambient glow of feverish excitement. Never before had I attacked household chores with such exuberance as I tried to make the flat look welcoming. As the time for Elaine to come into my life drew closer and closer I'm sure the children thought the whole flat was a no-go area.

'Are you sure you want a biscuit?'

'Yes Mummy, I'm sure.'

'I don't really want you to have one.'

'Why not?'

'You'll drop crumbs on the carpet.'

* * *

'Mummy, Mummy,' Lisa cried. 'I don't want to play with Jackie.'

'Why not darling?' This was unusual, normally Lisa and Pat's youngest were inseparable.

Fat tears rolled down her cheeks. 'I've got a headache.'

I put her on my knee. She felt very hot and feverish and then I saw the rash. It was on her arms and had started to appear on her tummy.

That night Steven cried incessantly and by morning was showing the same symptoms. A visit to the doctors' confirmed that they both had German Measles. Normally such a childhood ailment would have been just a hiccup. Not rubella; my head wailed as I realised that Elaine couldn't come. She was seven weeks pregnant and to be exposed to the rubella virus in the early stages of pregnancy could be fatal.

Pat sat with the children, while I used her telephone to make the most difficult phone call I'd ever had to make.

'Elaine, you can't come,' my voice was flat, devoid of any animation as I struggled to suppress my disappointment.

But I couldn't hide it from Elaine.

'Why, what's wrong? Has something happened? She asked, her voice full of concern.

'Yes, no, I mean it's nothing to worry about. It's just that there's an epidemic of German Measles here and Lisa and Steven are ill at the moment, so I can't possibly let you come.' My voice trailed miserably down the electric wire, connecting Edinburgh and London.

'I can't believe it, I didn't think anything could go wrong this time. I know we're disappointed but you're so right to stop me from coming. You know, for a few moments I wondered how the children having German Measles could possibly interfere with our reunion.' There was a slight pause. 'Try not to be unhappy Mary, we will meet; I promise.'

Light flooded into me. The connecting link between Elaine and myself was stronger than three hundred miles of electric cable, it was stronger than twenty-eight years apart, it was as strong as life itself.

PART TWO

"The first time ever I saw your face"

Roberta Flack – 1969

Chapter Twelve

The day I first met you, the sun rose hesitantly from a shadowy sky and wispy clouds hovered on the horizon. Keeping vigil from an upstairs window I watched serpentine droplets of water, left by an overnight shower, slide down the shiny glass and succumb to oblivion. Once or twice I rushed to check my face in the mirror. Nothing had changed; I looked terrible. A thyroid problem, coupled with little sleep, had left my eyes swollen and stained with black smudges. Physical contact with you would soon be a reality and my anxiety mounted as the minutes ticked away. The picture I carried on the brink of my consciousness curled at the edges until all that remained was an amorphous image of you. Surely it was you? It must be you. I was about to meet my other self and I didn't know either one of us.

'Why don't you come downstairs and relax. They won't be here for at least half an hour.' Tony's voice spiked my stream of consciousness.

Misgivings scurried like mice down the stairs. 'I can't wait for Elaine to come, but after all the years of waiting, now it's actually going to happen I'm gripped with uncertainties and fears and...' I hesitated, reluctant to voice the unthinkable. 'It's... it's as if I'm going to meet a stranger, why would I think that? What *is* wrong with me?' Doubts poured forth like emotional waterfalls and all Tony could do was attempt to stem the flow.

'Up until now you've only had a dream whereby you imagined what would happen; now you're facing reality head on it's a different story. Hopefully, when Elaine arrives you'll feel better.' He stopped, considering his words carefully. 'Darling, you have to realise it's completely new territory, and not just for you; we'll all have to make adjustments to our lives.'

I should have seen past his words and sensed his disquiet. But, I was too preoccupied with suffering a crisis of identity.

Lisa, dressed in a flowery, purple maxi-dress, tried to help.

'Mummy, do you think Sherry will like Aunty Elaine?' She asked, stroking our long-suffering cat.

From being a tiny kitten she had had to endure the indignity of being wrapped in a well-worn pink blanket and wheeled around in a doll's pram. As she grew older, and too big for the toy carriage, Sherry would leap out; only to be caught again and smothered with love.

'I'm sure she will darling,' I said, glancing down at the mixed-breed cat with half a white face. Sherry had hailed from Morningside, a classy area south of Edinburgh, whose owners were mortified when their pure Persian cat escaped and in the heat of the moment become pregnant. With childish innocence, Lisa had injected levity into the day. Ultimately, if the cat approves, any lingering doubts will be banished and we'll all live happily ever after.

Steven's comfort took a more boisterous form.

'Nenah, nenah, nenah. Watch out Mum, you're going to get smashed up.'

Since Tony had joined the police force, the hallway had become home to criminal getaway cars, closely pursued by police vehicles, all culminating in horrific crashes. 'Do you think Kristy will want to play with my cars?' Steven asked, head bent, concentrating on the grisly carnage.

'Um, I'm not sure darling, she's only two years old. But you can give one to her, if you want to.'

'Not to keep?' Steven exclaimed.

'No, no just to play with while she's here.'

'Yeah, okay.'

He returned to his rescue mission and I ascended the stairs once more.

I waited. Ten minutes elapsed. I waited. A metallic, pale green estate car swept around the corner, gliding smoothly to a halt outside our front garden gate. The symmetry of the wheel hubs gleamed in the sunlight. Then I saw you. I stared in fascination at your face. It was my face, without the bad bits. The colour of your hair matched mine, but the chic style screamed sophistication. In contrast, my mane tumbled to my shoulders in hippy disarray. As the low hum of the car's engine died away and the passenger door began to open, I felt unable to move.

Chapter Thirteen

'They're here.' Three voices yelled from below.

'Yes, I know.' I whispered.

Attempting to expunge my earlier uncertainties, I rushed headlong down the stairs, only one certainty in my mind; I must be the first one to see you.

I opened the front door, unfastened the gate and approached the car, to be greeted by your smiling face and a pale yellow suit similar to one I owned; except mine was the high street version. My face smiled in mirror image. You seemed so sophisticated, so confident; I felt awkward and self-conscious in comparison. We were locked in a vacuum as time galloped to a crawl. I stared in wonderment at your long, lush eyelashes which swept your cheeks. We were supposed to be identical twins for goodness sake, where were *my* glamorous eyelashes?

Christian was busy un-strapping Kristy from her seat and taking out a baby seat which held your latest tiny bundle, Sacha, who had arrived six weeks premature.

Elaine took my hands and kissed me on both cheeks. 'We've made it at last,' she said simply.

'Yes,' I agreed. 'Did you have any difficulty finding us?'

'Not really, we took one wrong turn, but otherwise no problems.'

'Let's go inside, you must be dying for a coffee.'

'Absolutely, my caffeine levels definitely need a boost,' she laughed.

The conventional conversation to herald your arrival clung to the air like an odd ritual. *Say something meaningful*, I thought. But instead I ushered everyone inside. Lisa and Steven clustered around me and Kristy, delicate as a porcelain doll, clasped Elaine's skirt tightly. Tony and Chris – as Elaine called her husband – shook hands and then Chris took my hand in a very Gallic way. I thought for a moment he was going to kiss it, but he kissed me on both cheeks.

'I am very pleased to meet wiz you. It ees really weird, you look and sound ze same,' he said in his heavily accented English.

'I'll make the drinks,' I said, my voice stilted and unnatural.

Elaine followed me into the kitchen. Bright orange curtains hung at the windows and natural rush matting covered the floor. Switching on the kettle I turned to her.

'I was so apprehensive before you came, no,' I contradicted myself. 'I was totally terrified. It was as if... as if I was about to meet some stranger instead of my own twin sister,' I concluded nervously, expecting Elaine to look shocked.

On the contrary, she nodded her head in agreement.

'That's exactly how I felt, I'm so pleased it wasn't just me.'

'Really?' She looked and sounded so self-assured.

'Really. I was a bundle of nerves in the car, and when we took the wrong turning I was convinced we'd never get here. Then I thought perhaps it would be for the best if we didn't. Honestly Mary, what a pair!'

We laughed together and our qualms disappeared into the ether.

'By the way,' I said, 'your eyelashes are brilliant, how do you get them to look so good?'

Her eyes twinkled. 'They're not real, I've been wearing false eyelashes forever. Well, since I started working at the theatre when I was sixteen, but it feels like forever. In the sixties everyone wore them, especially in the theatre, you wouldn't have been seen dead without them. Of course, since I've had the children I haven't had time to mess about, but I thought, as this is a special day,' she paused, as we both realised the magnitude of the occasion. 'Besides, my own eyelashes are nowhere near as thick as they used to be,' she continued. 'Mum told me it would ruin them, but of course I never listened,' Elaine finished gaily.

'I wouldn't care if my eyes looked like yours.'

'But they do.'

'Yeah, right...'

Elaine sat at the formica kitchen table, while I took coffee from the cupboard and began spooning it into the cups.

'Does Chris take sugar?' I enquired.

'Yes, one spoon for him and two for me please.'

'You take sugar in your drinks?' I asked in surprise.

Elaine gave me a puzzled look. 'Yes, why is it a problem?'

'No, no problem, it's just that I haven't taken sugar in drinks since I was eleven and I just thought... well I suppose I assumed that you wouldn't either.'

'Why did you stop taking sugar when you were eleven?' She asked in amazement.

'Because we had to give up sweets, chocolate and sugar for Lent. Then when Easter finally arrived, tea with sugar tasted horrible. Although I never liked tea anyway,' I said, pulling a face. 'Didn't you have to give up sweets for Lent?' I asked.

'Good, grief no. My mum would never have made me do that.'

'But you had to go to church?'

'I was brought up a Catholic and both my brothers were altar boys so I went to Mass with them, although I never understood the Latin, it meant nothing to me and then when I was ten...'

'What, every week?' I couldn't help interrupting.

'Yes, why?'

'Because my mother said that… "No Mary, don't go there" It's just you would think we might have seen each other at Mass,' I improvised.

'No we wouldn't have, because mum said you attended The Annunciation and we always went to that tiny church in Newbold Village.'

'I didn't know that. Sorry, you were saying.'

'Basically when I was ten one of my friends, who attended Sunday School at the Methodist Chapel asked me if I'd like to go with her. It sounded much more fun than going to Mass.'

'I don't suppose you were allowed to go?' I said, imagining the furore if I'd ever contemplated such an outrageous mortal sin.

'Mum wasn't very happy at first, but she usually gave in to me, then when I was eleven I told her I didn't want to go to church anymore because I didn't believe in it.'

I was having difficulty comprehending this scenario. 'What did she say?' I asked, shocked yet spellbound.

'She was fine about it, said I was old enough to make up my own mind and perhaps I'd feel differently when I was an adult. Mum is very liberally-minded in her views. I often tell her she was born before her time,' Elaine finished.

'You sound really close to your mum,' I said wistfully.

'Oh yes, we are, in fact, I don't know how I'd have managed without her these past few months with all the traumas, particularly not knowing if Sacha was going to survive. But she did thank goodness. Mum's lovely, you'll like her. She always feels so guilty because she didn't adopt you as well, but their circumstances were not good and….'

The children came running into the kitchen at that moment, and our conversation was suspended in time.

I needed to know everything about your life, about your family, about our circumstances. For now my curiosity would have to wait.

The day had been triumphant; and the cat liked you.

Chapter Fourteen

The following day I walked around encased in euphoria.

After taking Lisa and Steven to school I ventured into Boots and surveyed the two types of false eyelashes on display.

'Are these the only ones you have?' I enquired of the sales assistant.

'Yes, we don't have much call for them around here.'

'No I suppose you don't,' I replied.

I chose a pair whose label assured me, would transform my whole look into one of Hollywood glamour.

Back home, I applied them clumsily to my upper lids – it wasn't as easy at it appeared – and appraised myself critically in the mirror. I was literally being you, but looked nothing like you. I resembled a cross between Ermintrude the cow and a Pantomime Dame. There was no parallel between my puffy eyes and enigmatic allure, plus, the lashes were extremely uncomfortable. Undeterred I persevered, ignoring strange looks from the children, until Tony came home from work later that evening.

'What on earth have you got on your eyes?' He queried.

'False eyelashes, do you like them?' I said, fluttering them painfully as opposed to provocatively.

'No, I do not, they look awful. What on earth made you buy them?' He replied.

Even though I knew they did, I couldn't help feeling wounded by his reaction.

'Elaine was wearing them yesterday and she looked great,' I retorted.

'Did she? I can't say I noticed.'

'You must have done. And surely if they suit Elaine, they must suit me.'

'You're not Elaine,' he said. 'Anyway, I prefer you the way you are, not all made up to the nines.'

'But, I'm her twin sister...' I paused before continuing. 'Don't you like her?' I asked, suddenly filled with foreboding.

'Yes, I like her, but her life is so different from yours; you can't possibly try to emulate everything she does, or says,' he replied.

'But you do like her?' I persisted

'Yes, of course. Now what's for dinner, I'm starving.'

It wasn't until many years later that Tony admitted first to himself, and then to me that he had been jealous of Elaine. Prior to her presence in our lives, Tony and the children were the only close family I had, and he was the first person I turned to. Elaine had usurped his position and could potentially become my closest confidant. In the fullness of time, I understood. But not today. I felt no empathy for his inner turmoil.

Chapter Fifteen

With jobs and families to juggle, one to one contact was difficult. But the few times we managed to spend alone were productive, and gradually the thirty year void began to fill up. The fragmented formation of our lives, hitherto unknown, began to slot into place like the lost pieces of a puzzle.

Elaine told me what she knew about the circumstances surrounding our birth, scanty details, but far more than I had ever known. In 1945 at the end of WWII, Elaine's dad, Paddy, who had been wounded during the war was billeted at the boarding house where our natural mother, Leah, was staying after giving birth to us. He thought she was nineteen years old and said she'd been disowned by her family, subsequently leaving her destitute. We slept in a drawer and were wrapped in blankets which people generously donated.

Paddy immediately fell in love with these two tiny, black-haired babies, and willingly helped with feeding and bathing. Returning home at the weekends, he eulogised to his wife about the twins.

'Oh, you should see them Lavinia, they're gorgeous. You would love them.'

Lavinia, petite and pretty with short dark hair, picked at an invisible thread on her neat, blue skirt. 'Yes, you're right I would.' Sadness clouded her eyes. She had tried to forget, for the sake of her two sons Vincent and Kevin, but how could she ever forget her beautiful little girl, Theresa, who had died at just eighteen months old, and later the baby boy who'd been stillborn.

Paddy's voice broke through her unhappy thoughts.

'You know they're going to be put into a Jewish children's home?'

Lavinia's heart went out to them.

'Why don't you take the baby clothes back with you? There are some beautiful dresses among them, it's probably best they be put to good use.'

Paddy knew the pain she would feel giving up the baby clothes. It reaffirmed what he'd always known; she had a heart of gold.

Paddy said suddenly. 'Do you think there's any way we could afford to adopt them?'

Lavinia looked up in surprise. 'If only we could, but I can't see how, money is so tight at the moment, it's a struggle to feed and clothe Kevin and Vincent as it is.' Lavinia already had two jobs to supplement their income, until Paddy was de-mobbed and could find a job.

Paddy sat forward in his seat. 'I've just had an idea, maybe we could adopt just one of them; I'm sure we could manage. Then at least one baby will have a family to love her. What do you think?' He asked, gazing intently at his wife, willing her to agree.

A gleam of hope crept into Lavinia's hazel eyes, then died. 'I don't know Paddy. Do you think it would be fair to split them up? In any case, it's probably just a pipe dream, it's doubtful the authorities would allow it.'

Paddy stayed silent, his mind turning over and over, trying to figure out a solution.

* * *

The following week Paddy returned to Leeds and at the first opportunity he spoke to Leah. He found her in the kitchen, staring through the grimy window at the featureless back yard. He put the proposition to her. At first she thought he intended to adopt them both, but when she realised it was only one, her disappointment showed. She wasn't sure and besides she didn't think it would be legal. Paddy, not easily deterred, said he thought they should ring the children's home where Leah planned to place her twins. Incredibly, after much debate with the authorities concerned, they decided the twins could be split up, but only if their mother agreed and another family could be found to adopt the other twin. Leah consented.

Paddy returned home victorious and Lavinia, caught up in a vortex of excitement, planned immediate action to find another family. As a devout Catholic her first consideration was that the other baby must go to good Catholic people. Tomorrow afternoon she would be attending the Mothers' Union meeting at the Church Hall, as she normally did, and where better to find someone? She thought.

Remarkably, her expectations were fulfilled. She found Doris Black. She had one daughter, aged ten, and had been contemplating adoption for a while. Lavinia only knew the lady by sight, but she seemed quite interested as she listened to Lavinia's proposal. Although her manner appeared a little brusque, Lavinia was certain of her devout Catholicism. Consequently, the baby would be brought up in a loving, God-fearing home. Lavinia proceeded to tell Mrs. Black everything she knew about the twins, saying she understood that Mrs. Black would have to discuss it with her husband. She explained that if they were serious about adopting the other twin, they should contact the relevant authorities as soon as possible, or the twins would be taken into the orphanage. Lavinia wrote down all the details on a piece of paper and handed it to Mrs. Black.

When they next met, it was agreed that Mr. and Mrs. Black definitely wanted to adopt one of the twins, but there were stipulations. Mrs. Black insisted that the child she adopted would have to attend St. Mary's – the only Catholic school in the area. Owing to the fact that she wanted no contact between the twins, Lavinia must therefore, send her child to a different school. Mrs. Black was resolute; the twins must be kept totally apart since it would be "better for everyone concerned". Lavinia was shocked, having assumed the twins would have close contact, particularly at school and church. However, Lavinia was so desperate to adopt one of the twins, and terrified Mrs. Black would pull out of the arrangement that she agreed, dismissing doubts which nibbled at the edge of her mind. It seemed terribly important to Mrs. Black, so keeping a sense of proportion, she consoled herself by rationalising that not everyone thought as she did. Lavinia didn't worry too much about her child having to go to a non-Catholic school, she felt God would find her wherever she was. She prayed for a satisfactory outcome.

Chapter Sixteen

Elaine looked at me sadly when she had finished. 'I'm sorry Mary, it obviously wasn't as satisfactory as my mum thought. I know she said the time we saw you in town when I was small... can you remember I mentioned it when we first spoke on the phone?'

'Yes, I remember.'

'Well, mum told me when I was older, you looked so unhappy and both Vince and Kev kept asking why she hadn't adopted you as well. She feels terribly guilty.'

'Honestly Elaine, there's no need, it wasn't that bad. What is awful is what my mother said about, about...' I'd spoken without thinking.

'About what?'

Usually we told each other everything, but I didn't want to hurt her. 'Oh, it doesn't matter now.' I said, regretting my earlier insensitivity.

'No, tell me, I want to know everything, good and bad,' she replied.

So I told her how contemptuous my mother had been about her family. They weren't good Catholics, they took the biggest baby and the best baby clothes before my mother and father arrived and last, but not least that, 'You were a bad lot because they let you run around doing exactly what you wanted, and I was to have nothing to do with you.'

Elaine was upset for her parents.

'What dreadful things to say, she didn't even know them. Kev was so excited about having a new baby sister that mum let him choose; and he chose me. But it could just as easily have been you. As for the baby clothes, like I said, mum had sent those in the first place so they were only taking back what belonged to them. She doesn't sound a very nice person, it's no wonder you don't see her.'

'I used to think a lot of the problems stemmed from my being a difficult child, which I was, but some of the things she said and did when I was older are more difficult to disregard. It's only since I've been estranged from her that Tony told me the last thing she said to him when he was leaving our house to fly to Singapore. She told him that she "hoped my plane crashed". Her warped reasoning being, that he would never have me.'

Elaine looked aghast and put an arm around me. 'My God, what an awful thing to say, no wonder you didn't dare to search for me. It was so different for me, mum told me at a very early age – even before I could speak properly – that I was adopted and had a twin sister. I always remember, she told me that having a twin sister made me very special, and you know Mary, I've always felt very special.' She smiled at me.

I returned her smile. 'But you still haven't told me if you were bad?'

Chapter Seventeen

'Ah, well that's another matter,' she laughed. 'It depends upon your definition of bad, you considered Jimmies synonymous with Dante's Inferno. It was mum who persuaded me and my friend to go there because we were mad about jiving; probably because we drove her crazy with the music. But there was nothing terrible about it, we just enjoyed ourselves.'

'I used to love jiving too, when I was older, but you must only have been about eleven,' I remarked, filled with admiration for her wanton behaviour.

'Yes, that's right, at the time dancing filled our lives. All three of us danced from an early age. Vince won a scholarship and was offered a place at Sadler's Wells but in the end he chose The Ballet Rambert; which is why we moved to London. Vince went on to do really well in the West End; he danced in the Cliff Richard films and of course did quite a bit of television. Mum sent me to dancing school when I was three because I was so timid and shy.'

'Were you? I thought I was the diffident one.'

'Oh yes, mum said I was terrible, but it obviously worked because I did loads of stage shows when I was quite young. I can remember often travelling to Sheffield on the train on my own. I became so confident in my dancing and I was determined to make the stage my career, I was even going to call myself Elaine Hamilton.' She laughed at the memory. 'Until Vince took me to the theatre and I saw what a hard life it was for such little remuneration; so I decided against it. Even so, I found the theatre irresistible, which is why I ended up working in the box office at the Adelphi Theatre. Did you know I was the youngest box office manageress in London at the time?'

'No, I only knew you worked there.'

'The London Evening Standard did a piece about it because I was only twenty-one,' Elaine said, quite rightly sounding proud of this achievement.

'Did you meet any stars?' I asked, basking in second-hand glory.

'Can you remember Anna Neagle? She starred in *Charlie Girl* at the Adelphi. She was lovely. We invited her to our wedding but unfortunately she was doing television and couldn't make it. And, of course there was Tommy Steele, he was your typical cockney, and not forgetting Joe Brown who was also in *Charlie Girl* for a while; he was great fun. Mind you, I'd met quite a few others before then. My friend Dee and I used to go to the 2i's coffee bar in Soho, bet your mum would think that was bad...' she said mischievously, 'where a lot of the sixties groups started. Oh, and not forgetting George Chakiris, Vince introduced me to him when he was starring in West Side Story. He was gorgeous, it was love at first sight on my part as if he'd fancy me.' Elaine laughed and made a face. 'But the one that thrilled me the most was meeting Judy Garland. She was performing in two concerts at The London Palladium and Harold Fielding, my boss, brought her to the Adephi. She was very gracious and so charismatic I feel so privileged to have met her,' Elaine finished, a faraway look in her eyes as she remembered these halcyon days.

'Talking about film stars,' I said. 'When I was five I was convinced there was a photograph of me outside the Regal Cinema: tell me it was you Elaine, because if it wasn't I've been living in a dream world for most of my life.'

'Gosh, yes it was me, I'd forgotten about that. I think mum's still got the photograph. They were doing a promotion for Patricia Dainton, and my dancing teacher, Audrey, supplied some of her pupils to be photographed with her. They needed a very small child and Audrey thought of me. All I remember is being hauled out of bed and mum taking out those awful rags she used to tie my hair up in every night so I'd have beautiful ringlets,' Elaine said, raising her eyebrows in derision.

'I knew it was you, even though I didn't know, if you see what I mean,' I said. Then added, 'I wouldn't have minded having rags in my hair if I'd been allowed to have it long.'

'Honestly, it was a real pain Mary, I'm sure that's why I keep my hair short these days.'

'That's why I have mine long.'

We both laughed at the irony.

We were companionably silent for a few moments.

'Do you ever think you would like to try and find our real mother?' I asked.

'No, I've no desire at all, my mum is the only mum I'll ever have,' she answered firmly. 'Why, would you?'

'I don't know, well no, that's not true I have thought about it sometimes. It's probably because I wasn't close to my mother that I do wonder about her. It must have been difficult for her in those days, particularly if her family were Jewish Orthodox; they wouldn't have had any sympathy for an unmarried pregnant girl,' I said.

'Yes, I know what you mean, but I'm not sure she was that bothered about us. Dad said other people in the house seemed to take more care of us than she did,' Elaine replied.

I couldn't believe she didn't care about us. 'Maybe she was suffering from depression. It must be hard having two babies crying to be fed at the same time, especially at night.' Another thought struck me. 'Maybe she didn't want to get too attached to us, knowing we were going into a home.'

'You could be right of course, but maybe we'll never know the truth. Actually, I am curious to know who our father is, aren't you? Elaine said.

95

'I suppose I am, but I just feel that whoever he is, he just went off and left her literally holding the babies. Unless of course, he didn't know about us.' I started to giggle.

'What?'

'Because it was wartime, Tony is convinced that our real father was either an Italian prisoner of war or an American GI. Actually, I think I'll go for the former, because I'm always being mistaken for Italian.'

'Do you know Mary, I'm often told I look Italian. Either that or some of the Americans who came to the theatre used to say: "Well Gee, don't you look just like Barbara Streisand".' Elaine grimaced and said, 'Another thing I used to get, was, "what's a charming Yiddisher girl like you doing working here? You'd make a lovely wife for my son". Anyway we digress, as usual, to get back to our real mother, if you want to try and find her don't let me deter you.'

'I suppose the estrangement from my mother made me think about it. But, now I've got you it doesn't seem as important, although I must admit to being curious. I'll send for my original birth certificate and maybe look into it just to satisfy my inquisitive nature,' I replied lightly.

* * *

To this end I sought out an organisation called N.O.R.C.A.P.; a group set up in 1982 to help whom they termed The Adoption Triangle: birth parent, adoptee and adopter. They were extremely interested in the fact that I had been reunited with my twin sister and asked if I would write a piece for their newsletter. This I duly did and promptly forgot about it.

One day I received a telephone call which put all thoughts of searching for our natural mother out of my head. It changed my relationship with you. For the first time I was able to see into your soul; and I saw the mirror image in mine.

**Elaine (on table) with actress Patricia Dainton
Circa 1950**

Elaine aged 22

Mary aged 20

Mary aged 19

Elaine, aged 29

Chapter Eighteen

The telephone rang. It was Pam, the Chairperson of N.O.R.C.A.P.

'Hi Mary, have you booked your holidays yet?'

It seemed a strange opening gambit.

'Er, yes we're going to Mallorca. Why?'

'When are you going?' she said, ignoring my query.

I felt slightly disconcerted; whenever I spoke to Pam it usually concerned N.O.R.C.A.P. business. 'In August. Why?' I asked again.

'How would you like to go to America in September?' She answered, her voice laden with intrigue.

The notion of visiting America had long been an idealistic dream, but idealism doesn't equate into money.

'I'd love to go to America, Pam, but with two teenagers to feed and clothe, it's not on the agenda I'm afraid.'

'An all expenses paid trip is on the agenda for you and Elaine if you're interested...' she paused dramatically.

'Is this some kind of joke?' I asked cautiously.

'No, honestly, Mary. You know the article you wrote for our newsletter?'

'Yes.'

'Well you won't believe it, but I've been contacted by John Stroud. He's the assistant director of Social Services for Hertfordshire and apparently he counsels adopted children who are searching for their natural parents. Occasionally, he finds a missing twin and it's in this context he's become involved with Professor Thomas Bouchard Jnr. of Minnesota University, who heads the 'Nature versus Nurture' Research Programme there. Evidently, they're always looking for twins; particularly identical twins who were reared apart. They're more likely to find them here in Europe because of the war years. John was very excited when he saw your article, and wants to know, as soon as possible, if you and Elaine would be willing to participate in the research programme. I take it you might be interested?' She finished.

I was reeling with excitement. 'Are you kidding! It sounds like the opportunity of a lifetime.' Ironically making two in mine. 'I'll ring Elaine straight away but I know she'll say yes,' I said breathlessly.

'Great, I'll give you John's number so you can get the ball rolling. Oh, and don't forget to let me know how you get on,' she said before hanging up.

It's not often a telephone call lasting a few minutes can change your life.

* * *

The weeks that followed were a blur of telephone calls, letters and arrangements. John Stroud and research team members, who rang from America, went to great lengths to impress upon us the strenuousness of the tasks involved with the research. The post brought reams of information including the project description of the 'Minnesota Study of Twins Reared Apart'. This outlined the study, which both Elaine and I agreed looked extensive. We giggled over eminent names, Professors Tuna, Till, Tellegen and Knobloch. Our imaginations running high, we felt about to be plunged into a world littered with Dickensian characters. However, our resolve to go was unanimous and we blithely agreed to everything; after all how hard could it be? We didn't realise at this juncture what the ramifications would be; and that was probably just as well.

Professor Bouchard, the Director of the Psychology Department, even rang himself. He told us we were allowed to bring our husbands, but there was a proviso; both husbands must participate in order for parallels to be drawn. Regrettably, Chris objected strongly, stating he couldn't possibly leave his work for ten days and fly off to America. He had recently moved to manage a different hotel outside Sheffield, and they now lived in a lovely detached house, once again in Chesterfield. Elaine had confided to me that they were having problems and she strongly suspected Chris of having an affair with a young woman at work; which he vehemently denied. I felt it was unfair because it meant Tony couldn't go.

A few days later as we sat having coffee, Tony said, 'I can't say I'm not disappointed. I'd love to go to America, but, ultimately, I think it will be good for you and Elaine to spend some time together on your own.'

I was surprised, even though I knew he now accepted Elaine as part of our lives, I wasn't sure he exactly welcomed her with open arms.

'That's really considerate of you to see it from that viewpoint. I must confess, what with all the arrangements I hadn't thought much beyond boarding the plane in time; but, yes it will be nice to have time to ourselves. Even so, Chris could go if he wanted, because Elaine said someone would come in to manage the hotel for ten days.' I paused, thinking maybe Elaine was right. 'Do *you* think Chris is having an affair?'

Tony stayed silent for long moments and looked uncomfortable.

'Well, I probably shouldn't tell you this…' he stopped. 'Whatever you do, don't breathe a word to Elaine.'

'Tell me what?' I asked full of foreboding.

'Chris is definitely having an affair… he told me.'

'He told you? What did you say?' I was outraged.

'I warned him, he was being stupid and that he will lose Elaine and the girls if he carries on. But he said it was no big deal. He provides money to keep the family, so it doesn't matter what he does in his spare time. He also said it's accepted in France that men have their mistresses.' Tony drank his coffee before continuing. 'I told him he could be in for a shock, because English culture is totally different and he's heading for disaster.'

'How did he respond?'

'He said I was worrying unnecessarily and that everything would be fine. To be honest, I get the impression that this woman isn't the first and she won't be the last.'

'You're right, I can't tell Elaine,' I said worriedly. 'But then again, I ought to tell her; she suspects anyway and it isn't right him carrying on this charade of happy families. Elaine says he's always out, ostensibly on work related business and Kristy and Sacha hardly ever see him, and when they do he's never got time for them.' I was feeling angrier by the minute.

'Please don't pass on any of this to Elaine, I would hate to be the one to upset her,' Tony said anxiously. He really cared about Elaine. It pleased me.

'No okay, I won't tell her at the moment, only because it will spoil our trip to America for her. She knows to a degree anyway and I feel sure she'll sort it out when we come back.' I had another thought. 'No wonder she's got a thyroid problem.' – she'd been having treatment for a few months now – 'If you remember, mine started through the upset with my mother when we returned from Singapore.'

'Talking of which,' Tony said, changing the subject. 'Did you get your medical report from the doctors?'

It was three weeks since I'd requested it. 'It'll be ready tomorrow,' I replied. The Research team required all documentation pertaining to our births and medical histories. Why the surgery needed time to prepare mine, was beyond me. When it finally came; it contained one line.

Underwent Partial Thyroidectomy – Hashimoto's disease detected at time of operation.

Hashimoto's Disease? What on earth was that? It was the first I'd heard about it and I began to feel decidedly queasy.

'It sounds like something you'd catch in "Tenko" Mum,' Lisa said, highly amused.

We'd been watching a television programme about the appalling conditions of women who'd been taken prisoners by the Japanese during the war.

'Yes, very funny, but have you thought, it could be something hereditary,' I replied ominously.

'Ugh, I hadn't thought of that,' she said.

'Well, it can't be much, I feel fine and you all seem normal, well as normal as you'll ever be,' I finished, departing quickly before the cushion hit me.

Chapter Nineteen

It was the middle of the night when we boarded the coach bound for Heathrow Airport. All the passengers were either dozing or gazing listlessly out at the damp grey hedgerows lulled by the soporific swish of the tyres on hard tarmac; except you and me. At thirty-eight years old we were behaving like children going on our first holiday to the seaside. We spoke softly, in deference to our fellow travellers, but as time marched towards dawn, we realised that everyone within earshot, was listening to our conversation.

Our discourse had started out innocuously enough, but it wasn't long before we were discussing our, identical, problematic bowels before moving on to Chris's infidelities.

'He swore on the children's lives he isn't having an affair,' Elaine said. 'He says it's all in my head and I'm imagining everything.'

'It sounds like he's playing mind games with you.' Knowing what I knew, I could have strangled him.

'You're exactly right, sometimes I even believe him and think that maybe I'm losing my mind. But you always know if something is wrong when you've been married for as long as we have.'

'Your gut instinct is usually right. What are you going to do?' I asked, hoping it was something positive.

Elaine sighed. 'Well first I'm going to enjoy this trip, even if it kills me, which according to everything they've told us, it may well do.' We both stifled our giggles. 'When I get home

I'm going to get to the bottom of it, even if I have to hire a private detective.'

At this juncture, a man dressed in a brown raincoat and slouchy hat, left his seat further down the coach and sat in the empty seat immediately in front of us. We exchanged glances, both knowing what the other was thinking. We tried to suppress the laughter which bubbled up inside of us, not very successfully. Fortuitously, the coach was turning into terminal four and we covered our hilarity by gathering our belongings together.

Elaine whispered to me as we rose from our seats. 'He must lead a very unexciting life if he has to listen to our conversation.'

'Well look at it this way, we might have made his day.'

'Or, he could be a private eye,' was Elaine's rejoinder.

In high spirits, we descended the steps of the coach into the misty light of daybreak.

* * *

The plane banked and commenced it's descent into Minneapolis. From the air, Minneapolis and its twin city, St. Paul, ranged over a vast area, cut at its core by the twisting ribbon of the Mississippi. We were met at the airport by Professor Thomas Bouchard. Jr. Not the grey, serious fellow, steeped in academia we'd expected, but a big bear of a man with a hearty laugh, sporting braces. As soon as he saw us he was thrilled, stopping short of rubbing his hands together with glee. Naively, we assumed it was our personal charisma, however, it transpired that identical twins reared apart were a rarity.

'You guys must be identical. Obviously, we'll confirm your status when we do the tests, but hey, I'd put money on it,' he boomed.

'We are identical,' Elaine said. 'Well everyone always thinks so. Although we looked more identical when we were younger.'

'You did bring photographs?' The professor asked and we both nodded.

'Great. I'm fairly sure you are identical. However, you'll come to learn that everything, and I mean everything, has to be investigated and probed in order to be proven, that way we are one hundred percent sure that our research into Nature versus Nurture is correct.'

I felt a momentary twinge of unease which I quickly dismissed.

He led us to his car, a modest Toyota, and we joined the freeway with its countless lanes and rushing traffic.

Leaning slightly forward in the back seat of the car, I chose the wrong moment to speak.

'Actually, Professor Bouchard could you…'

'Please call me Tom, everyone does,' he interjected, turning round with a genial smile on his face.

The question froze in my throat as the car sped towards the slip road, seemingly about to be sliced in two by the exit barrier. Elaine and I automatically clung to each other trying to squeak out a warning. At the very last second Tom's attention returned to his driving and we missed the barrier by a hairs breadth.

Totally unperturbed, Tom said, 'You were going to ask me something Elaine?'

'I'm Mary.'

''Hell, I guess I'll be able to distinguish you before too long.'

Personally, I didn't think it was going to be difficult, Elaine's hair was shorter than mine. But, unsettled by the near miss, I'd forgotten the question and Tom was busy pointing out buildings of interest, one of which stretched skyward, totally covered in musical notes. Soon we pulled up in front of a typical downtown hotel, The Hotel Leamington. Sun blazed down from a clear blue sky and embraced us as we emerged from the car; within seconds our travelling clothes clung to us like wet suits. It was Friday afternoon and Tom explained we would be allowed Saturday off and thereafter would be picked up at 7.00am sharp and be taken, by limo, to the university. Elaine and I looked at each other, we liked the sound of the limo but definitely not the crack of dawn start. But we said nothing. After pointing us in the right direction for the centre of downtown Minneapolis, he left us with a cheery wave and a last minute instruction.

'Don't forget, if the weather doesn't suit, just wait five minutes.' With that he was gone.

Chapter Twenty

The hotel had once been quite grand, but Elaine noted with a professional eye that it could benefit from a refurbishment. We rode the elevator to the ninth floor, in England we would have taken the lift, but being advocates of the old adage "when in Rome" we adopted the native idiom.

Entering the room where our luggage was already installed, we looked around what was to be our home for ten days. There were two large single beds covered with deep blue bedspreads trimmed with gold. Elegant gold, spiral standard lamps stood beside each bed, matching the overhead light and picture frames. The decoration was refined and subdued and we felt relaxed and secure.

'Right, lets get some room service,' Elaine said.

'Oh, do you think we should?' I always tended to be diffident in these matters.

Elaine looked at me in surprise. 'Why not? That's what this extensive menu is for,' she said waving a large white card in the air. 'Now let's see, yes, here it is.'

'Mmm, coffee, sounds great.' I was warming to the lifestyle by the second.

Elaine looked up, telephone receiver in mid air. 'Of course, you knew I meant coffee.'

'Sure did pardner,' I said, saluting smartly.

Despite the overnight journey and the eleven hour flight, we were raring to get out into the sun and explore. After telephoning our families to let them know we'd arrived safely, we donned shorts and tops and set off for downtown Minneapolis.

'I feel like one of the *Famous Five,*' I said gaily.

'Why?'

'Well, you know, we could be enacting The Terrible Twins' American Adventure.'

'Yeah, right. I can see now why your mother thought you had your head in the clouds.'

'Don't push your luck,' I responded, just as huge raindrops splashed onto our heads. A blustery wind suddenly whipped up from nowhere and we were being pelted with hailstones. The temperature signs above the street, had plummeted from 31°C to 17°C in the space of five minutes; just as Tom had predicted.

We still couldn't see any shops. 'Quick in here,' Elaine said, grabbing my arm. It was a towering skyscraper housing several corporate companies. However, no one challenged us so we sheltered until the worst of the rain had passed, shivering in our skimpy apparel. Contrary to our belief that Minneapolis was devoid of shops, we eventually found them inside vast buildings, interconnected by glass walkways. If our knowledge of geography had been better informed, we would have known it was the only way locals could survive the sub-zero temperatures, which could drop to as low as minus forty degrees in the winter months.

* * *

That night, we stood naked before the mirror and peered critically at our reflections. Two size ten bodies, but not devoid of flaws.

'You've got a mole like mine.'

'I prefer to call it a beauty spot,' Elaine responded. 'I used to emphasise this one with a black pencil.' She indicated the one above her upper lip.

I laughed softly. 'Yes, I've got that one too.'

'What's so funny?'

'I was thinking, you know I wasn't allowed to wear make-up, can you imagine if I'd applied black pencil then tried to rub it off before I arrived home, like I did with the eye shadow, I'd have been sporting a black moustache.'

Clinically, we checked for further identical marks.

'You've got larger breasts,' Elaine remarked.

'No I haven't.'

Elaine was adamant. 'Yes you have.'

'Okay, but your ankles aren't as skinny as mine, your knees aren't as knobbly and you're taller than me.'

Elaine squinted in the mirror. 'Yes, but even though our awful Jewish noses are the same, mine's bigger than yours.'

Our eyes met in the mirror and we collapsed with laughter, unable to believe our inanity. We laughed and laughed; until we cried.

Exhausted, we lay down in the comfortable beds. The interval of thirty-eight years since sleeping in a drawer – our first cradle – became nonexistent, the years swept away on a tide of discovery.

Chapter Twenty One

Six o'clock on the Sunday morning saw us sitting bleary-eyed eating breakfast.

'We'll be a size twenty by the time we get home if we carry on like this,' I said, wading through pancakes smothered in maple syrup.

'We need to try everything on the menu before we go home,' Elaine responded.

'Exactly, size twenty, like I said.'

The 'limo' arrived. What a disappointment. Elaine and I had visions of a stretch limousine driven by a courteous chauffeur. In reality, it was a glorified van with windows; similar to a people carrier. The driver was friendly and wearing a baseball cap.

The University of Minnesota was set in beautifully, landscaped grounds, the autumnal splendour of large trees creating a colourful backdrop. The Psychology Department into which we walked, felt hushed, as if in reverence to the academic genius within its confines.

I began to wonder nervously what I was doing here. What did I know about science and psychology? Absolutely nothing. St. Mary's didn't even teach science and anyway I would probably never have understood it. Where was the blithe spirit which had brought me here? I was certain Elaine would still have it, feeling totally at ease in this scholastic environment. Her education had been superior to mine and she knew about the arts; would knowing about the arts help? Elaine nudged me, pulling my thoughts back to reality.

'What do you think?'

'I can't think.'

Tom had come down from his office to greet us and he was so friendly and informative I began to feel stupid about my negative thoughts; but not as stupid as I was going to feel.

* * *

The primary research objective of the Minnesota Study of Twins Reared Apart is to study the relationship of medical and social life history differences between twins to current medical and psychological differences between them. [2]

Read quickly, this statement is concise, explains their aims and appears to pose no problem. Of course, reading and actually physically performing the prose are two different entities. Elaine and I were prepared to work long hours, we knew the medical teams would poke, prod and attach electrodes to any available piece of flesh and ask lots of questions. What we didn't know was that the programme was so rigorous some twins refused to co-operate with many of the tests, whilst one set even packed their bags and went home. We learned that numerous questionnaires were to be completed, involving thousands of questions. But these were to be done during any spare moments we had between sitting exams, life stress interviews, social life history interviews, sexual history analysis, strenuous physical exercises and medical screenings for just about every disease known to man.

---

[2] Project Description Minnesota Study of Twins Reared Apart, Dept., of Psychology, University of Minnesota. Minneapolis. U.S.A.

Tom introduced us to the three main members of his research team with whom we would be working closely.

'Hi there, I'm Nancy.' A slim young woman with swinging, straight brown hair and a wide smile, held out her hand.

'And I'm Kim. Would you like coffee?' The young woman was curvaceous with huge eyes.

'Yes, please,' Elaine and I said in unison. Having read the literature pertaining to the research, we knew Nancy and Kim were eminent doctor's, but they had no pretensions and made us feel at ease. The third person in the room was a young girl called Mary. Apparently, she was temporarily attached to the research programme, we presumed as a student of the university, acquiring practical experience. She was quiet with a natural sweet temperament.

The first few days were filled with mental ability tests, some being conducted via a computer, others written. Having never taken formal exams, I was beginning to feel as dense as a lisle stocking. Prior to commencing one written exam, Nancy instructed us to put our names on the top of the paper, complete one side and stop when she commanded. We then had to return the paper to her which she would subsequently hand back to us for completion. She was very firm that during the course of the examination we were not to speak. Stop watch in hand – she was very particular about her schedules – she asked us to commence.

After the first paper was completed she collected them and did whatever calculations were necessary, then handed them back. The stopwatch once again activated.

'Excuse me, Nancy,' I ventured.

'Shh, no talking.'

'But Nancy...'

'Mary, it will have to wait.'

Elaine joined in. 'Actually Nancy...'

'Now I know it's difficult for you two not to speak, but I really must insist on absolute sil...'

'But Nancy, I've got Elaine's paper.' I blurted out.

'Oh My Gard. Stop, quickly, stop.' Her voice rose two octaves, her hands wafting the air like two streamers caught in a breeze. 'Gee, how absolutely awful, if I'd let you carry on... Well, it doesn't bear thinking about.'

To our shame, Elaine and I started giggling, quite pleased for once it wasn't our blunder.

'Right, no talking or laughing, you may begin again.' The stopwatch clicked with a decisive clunk.

Chapter Twenty Two

Every night had seen us out on the town, making the most of the leisure time we had. There seemed little point visiting America if all we saw were medical instruments and exam papers. On the Wednesday night, however, we were given blood pressure monitors and told it would take our blood pressure every twenty minutes throughout the night. Slightly disconcerted by this news, we enquired if we'd get any sleep? Tom said airily, 'Hell, yes you'll be fine. I've never heard of anyone having a problem.'

Being confined to the hotel, we ate in their restaurant that evening. The food was excellent; we dined on fish and wild rice followed by blueberry tart, then retired to bed early to catch up on some reading. We reminisced for a while which had become a ritual. Elaine told me how disappointed she was at not being able to find me when we were twenty-one.

'I was quite upset going back to London on the train. I was so convinced I'd done the right thing waiting until we were twenty-one because of your parents, and so convinced I would see you. When I rang The Co-operative Insurance Office where you had worked and they told me you'd gone to live in Singapore, I couldn't believe it. I tried to persuade myself it was fate and we were destined never to meet.'

'I felt the same when I read the letter from Carolyn telling me you had rung. I kept thinking if only she'd given you my address.'

'To be fair, I probably didn't give her time to even react, I just said "thank you" and quickly hung up. All that was going around my head was that I'd missed you by three months and if only I'd have searched for you earlier. Not long after I returned to London Harold Fielding, my boss, told me about an impresario from New York who owned several Broadway theatres. Apparently, he'd asked if I could go and work for him for two years in New York because he was so impressed with the way I ran the box office at the Adelphi. He was losing a lot of money and wanted me to set up the same system in his theatres.'

'You never told me you worked in New York,' I exclaimed.

'No, that's because I didn't.'

'You didn't go? Why? I would have jumped at the chance.'

'Well, I did think about it, but at the end of the day I loved London and I loved my job at the Adelphi. It meant leaving all my family and friends, not to mention the brilliant social life, for New York where I didn't know anyone. In the end I turned it down.'

'Do you ever regret not going?' I asked.

'Occasionally, but then if I had I might have considered living there permanently and we'd probably never have met. I'm a great believer in everything happening for a reason.'

We decided to go to sleep earlier than usual, so attaching the rubber bandaging to our upper arms we set the machines to exactly the same time, as instructed.

'Despite what Tom said, I can't see we'll get much sleep with this happening every twenty minutes,' Elaine commented, trying to get comfortable.

'Well, perhaps it won't be too bad,' I replied, more in hope than expectation. 'Goodnight Elaine.'

'Goodnight Mary.'

Fifteen beautiful minutes elapsed.

'Oh my God,' I shot up in bed, my arm immobilised by a grip so tight I thought someone was trying to murder me.

'Whassamatter?' Elaine's voice blurred with sleep penetrated my pain. Nothing was happening with her monitor.

We settled down again.

'Ooh, ooh, that really hurts,' Elaine groaned.

'What do you mean? Mine's not doing anything.'

Quietness.

We started to fall asleep.

'EERG.' It woke Elaine.

'These machines are supposed to be synchronised.'

'Well maybe we should tell them.'

At this point we got out of bed and reset the machines, but to no avail they appeared to have a will of their own and quite frankly, I thought, had the look of a Dalek about them.

At three o'clock in the morning, I was the one who snapped first. Sitting up in bed I ripped the vile rubber bandage from my arm.

'Right I've had enough, we've got two and a half hours of precious sleep left before we have to get up and I can't stand anymore.' I sounded like a fractious child but tiredness had overtaken any rational thought.

Elaine was more reasonable. 'I'm not sure I can either, but do you think we ought to try and persevere for the sake of the research?'

'Look, we've co-operated with everything else, surely we're allowed to complain about something,' I grumbled. 'After all we haven't packed our bags and gone home.' Then I started to feel guilty. 'You're probably right though, they have paid for the trip and apart from the ten hours during the day, we're having a great time.'

But Elaine had now changed *her* mind. 'Actually, we'll be fit for nothing tomorrow,' she looked at her watch. 'Today even. Besides, the machines obviously aren't working properly so the readings will be all over the place, I doubt they'll be able to elicit any meaningful data.'

Gratefully, I acquiesced to your superior logic and we slept blissfully until the alarm awoke us at 5.30am.

Tom was disappointed, the whole team were disappointed. Even though they remained stoical in their disappointment, we felt like disobedient children. Later we took some consolation from the fact that childish behaviour among twins reared apart is a common characteristic. They said we were making up for the lost childhood spent apart. Well that was their explanation. Personally, I put it down purely to sleep deprivation.

Chapter Twenty Three

The day after the blood pressure debacle was less stressful but turned out to be embarrassing in the extreme for me and harrowing for Elaine.

We entered the research rooms and greeted Nancy, Kim and Mary like old friends; which is how we regarded them. Feeling somewhat cut off from the outside world, it was like being inside a bubble.

There was no sign of Tom. Kim sat on the edge of a desk drinking coffee from a polystyrene cup. 'Okay you guys, today we're going to be conducting some interviews. First up will be sexual history which we usually tape, assuming you have no objections?'

'I don't have a problem with that, do you Mary?' Elaine said turning to me.

'No, I don't think so.' I wasn't sure. Sexual matters had been taboo when I was growing up. I'd learned most of what I needed to know from my friend and a small amount from Ann, and only because she was ten years older and therefore knew more. Ultimately, any discussions involving sexual matters were limited to two people, Tony and Elaine.

Kim told Elaine she would be in an interview room with her and I would be going into another room with Mary. I was surprised, Mary seemed so young, but I dutifully followed her petite form into a room, where the only furniture was a plain wooden desk accompanied by two classroom chairs. Mary opened a drawer, took out a cassette and inserted it into a tape recorder. For a few minutes the only sound in the room was the clicking of buttons and whirring of celluloid as Mary rewound the tape. After a few minutes she broke the silence.

'You have the right to refuse answering any of the questions I ask. Naturally, we would like you to answer all of them and as fully as possible for our research. However, if at any time you feel uncomfortable I will stop the interview.' She smiled her sweet smile. 'You do fully understand, Mary?'

'Yes, I understand,' I answered, not understanding at all why they needed intimate details of my life.

Mary clicked the record button and began. 'At what age did you become sexually active?'

'Er, well perhaps a little, before I got married.'

'When you say a little, did you have full sexual intercourse?'

'No, I didn't,' I said firmly, thinking of the consequences if I had.

'So you were a virgin when you got married?'

'Yes, well sort of.'

'Sort of?' Can you be a little more explicit?'

This was one very switched on student. 'No not really, other than to say I wouldn't have dared to go any further because... well because I was terrified of becoming pregnant.'

'Why was that?' Mary asked kindly.

'First of all, my mother would have killed me and I know my father would have been upset. But the main reason was because I didn't want to end up a slut, so my mother could gloat over the fact that she'd been right all along. Anyway, I was a good Catholic girl,' I finished hurriedly. Hoping this would satisfy her.

Apparently it did because then she asked: 'Did you ever find yourself in a situation where you thought you would be raped or sexually assaulted?'

'No.' I wasn't about to tell her about my stupidity of dating someone ten years my senior when I was seventeen, and how lucky I felt to extricate myself from his van in one piece.

'Have you, or would you ever, consider sex with anyone other than an heterosexual partner?'

'Most certainly not.' The seemingly endless interrogation continued.

'Do you have sexual fantasies?'

'Excuse me?'

'Do you have a sexual fantasy?'

'Erm...' I paused. 'Erm... yes.'

'Could you tell me about it?'

'Well actually, I erm...' I paused even longer this time.

'Yes?' Mary encouraged.

I felt wretched. This was awful, surely she didn't expect me to answer?

The expectant look on her face told me otherwise. All I wanted to do was flee the room. Surely the earth wouldn't stop spinning because my innermost private fantasies weren't aired? The heavy silence crashed into the walls. Eventually I said. 'I'm very sorry Mary, I can't answer that question.'

'Oh, that's disappointing.'

I'll bet it is, I thought.

'It's so helpful if you can answer all the questions. Are you sure?' she persisted.

'Absolutely certain,' I replied.

'All right, not to worry, we've almost finished now,' Mary responded.

Thank you God.

As I reached the door Mary said, 'I forgot to mention, there must be no dialogue between you and Elaine regarding these interviews.'

In your dreams.

When Elaine emerged from her interview room a good ten minutes after me, she looked upset.

'What's wrong?' I asked, concern overriding my earlier discomfort.

'Don't worry, I'm okay. It's silly really, it was the question about rape and sexual assault, when I told Kim about my experience in Spain it brought it all flooding back.'

'You've never told me. What happened?' I asked in alarm.

'You know I used to go to Spain with Dee and her parents? During one holiday I'd been dating this Spanish boy for about a week. You know what it's like, a typical holiday romance.'

I nodded, having experienced one or two myself; I thought they were the best part of the holiday.

'I must have been so naïve, because one day whilst walking on the cliff tops he started kissing me, which was fine. But then, he began ripping viciously at my clothes, I couldn't believe it. I struggled with him and he became quite violent. I can remember thinking if he rapes me I will throw myself off the cliff. But somehow I managed to get away, it was as if I summoned up some super-human strength I didn't know I possessed.'

'How awful for you,' I said putting my arms around her. 'Are you sure you're all right?'

'Yes, I'll be fine, I honestly thought I'd forgotten about it, after all it was twenty years ago. Kim said it was locked away in my mind, but recounting the details has made it feel like it happened yesterday.'

'I know what you mean. It's not quite the same, but when we did the social history interview, going over all the old ground about my mother and my relationship with her, made me feel frightened and guilty again.'

'It's certainly dragged up stuff we'd prefer to forget,' Elaine said, with feeling.

We sat in silence for a few moments.

'Did you answer all the questions?' I asked her.

Without hesitation she replied, 'Yes, why?'

'Even the one about sexual fantasies?'

'Yes.'

'You didn't?'

'Of course I did,' Elaine answered with a hint of her mischievous smile. Without any preamble she filled me in, while I sat staring at her open mouthed.

'I always knew you were a bad girl,' I said laughing. There's no way I could answer that question, it was just too embarrassing. I must wear my inhibitions like a suit of armour, compared to you.'

'It's not surprising considering the way you were brought up, as I've said before, my mother was very liberally-minded.'

'By the way, did you know we weren't supposed to discuss anything?' I asked.

In answer, Elaine raised her eyebrows.

At the end of the day I thought I'd seen the last of my humiliation, but it was not to be. As we all descended in the elevator that evening, the conversation turned to age. It was revealed that Mary was thirty years old: we couldn't believe it.

Astounded, I said, 'We thought you were only about eighteen.'

'I bet you're not married Mary,' Elaine said chuckling.

Before Mary could reply, Tom said, 'You're right Elaine, she isn't married. It would hardly be fitting.'

'Why not? Lots of students are married,' Elaine said, looking puzzled.

'Because she's a nun,' he responded, obviously relishing the look of horror on my face.

'But... But... you interviewed me this morning for the sexual history,' I stammered, turning to Mary.

She nodded and smiled. The benign smile of a woman of the cloth.

Feeling even more disconcerted than when I'd been in the interview room, I addressed the whole team.

'That was underhand. How could you? If I'd known she was a nun I wouldn't have answered any of the questions.'

'Exactly.' Tom laughed. 'Why do you think we didn't tell you?'

Chapter Twenty Four

Professor Tom Bouchard was born in New Hampshire, but had little New England reserve. His outgoing personality touched everyone he came into contact with, including "his twins". He told us stories of triplets finding each other, and of twins separated at six months old, one brought up by his German mother, the other by his Jewish father in Trinidad. These accounts never ceased to amaze us, we felt they were so much more interesting than we were. But Tom said we were all unique, as only 300 sets of identical twins in the world had been separated. Although absent-minded professor would have been a misnomer for Tom, nevertheless, he did have some strange ideas.

On the day we were to undergo lengthy eye tests, Tom had informed us we would get part of the afternoon off and he would take us sight seeing. We were thrilled, time off *and* we could be tourists. Our enthusiasm was short lived. Before any examination of our eyes took place, drops were administered which would dilate the pupils. They did warn us that this procedure would impair our vision for a while.

By the time Tom picked us up, our eyes were extremely sore, we were half blind and both wearing dark glasses.

'Hi there. I thought we'd start with the Hiawatha Falls, visit a paddle steamer on the Mississippi and check out some of the beautiful lakes we have in the area. Then probably finish off with ice cream in the mall,' he intoned cheerfully.

'It all sounds very nice Tom, but we'd better take cameras, otherwise we won't have a clue what it looks like,' Elaine said, with mock innocence.

'Oh, you still can't see?' Before we could reply he carried on. 'I thought it might have worn off by now, although it is the reason you've got a free period. But hey, you'll have a great time.'

The truth dawned, obviously we'd been given the time off because we would be unable to fill in the ubiquitous questionnaires, or 'batteries' as they called them.

Despite the temporary disability, it was an unforgettable experience. We managed to see four of the fifteen thousand lakes, albeit not very clearly. A wedding was taking place at Hiawatha Falls, which created a romantic ambience that we felt, rather than saw. We chose blue ice cream, which as Elaine pointed out was garish enough for anyone to see. As the day finally grew to a close, our sight almost back to normal, we sat enjoying coffee. Tom was silent, but watching us closely.

'Is something wrong, Tom?' Elaine finally asked.

'You could say that. I'm sat here wondering just what you guys are talking about?'

We looked at him in surprise and I said, 'What do you mean Tom? We're speaking English the same as you.'

He leaned forward. 'Do you realise you're talking to each other using only one or two words? I can only assume that the two of you know what's going on, because I sure as hell don't.' Shaking his head he added, 'It's incredible.'

'Maybe you didn't quite catch everything we said because of our accents,' Elaine said diplomatically.

'I caught every word, but there wasn't enough of them.' He laughed.

'But we're not aware of doing anything like that, as far as we're concerned we're having a normal conversation.' I looked at Elaine for confirmation and she nodded.

'That's the great thing,' Tom was warming to his topic. 'You've absolutely no idea that you're communicating in this way, it's like a form of ESP.'

'That's ridiculous, we're just talking. Anyway, I don't believe in stuff like that.' Was Elaine's derisory reply.

'I'm telling you,' Tom said. 'You speak in half sentences and odd words to each other. You know, I've worked with twins for a long time but they never fail to surprise me. And do you know something else? I'm real envious of the special relationship twins have, it doesn't seem to matter how long they've been separated. In fact, I feel cheated by being born a singleton,' he boomed.

We discussed it that night.

Flopping down on the bed, I asked Elaine, 'Do you think we do that?'

'Well, I didn't think so, but Tom obviously does. I know I was cynical but I don't suppose he would make it up, he is an eminent professor.'

'True. But still, it sounds as if we read each other's minds and we don't.'

'I expect some people would think that's what we do. I must admit I'm finding it hard to find another explanation, aren't you?' Elaine said, removing her make-up.

'Yes I am, it's an enigma. At least we're together to be able to communicate, however people perceive it,' I replied.

Down the years our theories became a hazy memory but the enigma flourished to such an extent that Tony refers to it as "twin speak".

Chapter Twenty Five

Our sojourn in the United States was rapidly drawing to a close and tonight Elaine and I were going to hit the town. Tomorrow would be our last night but Tom had invited us to a party at his home, where we would meet all kinds of people whose whole lives appeared to revolve around twins. As we got ready to go out, we chatted about the days tests.

'I can't believe how excited they get about identical teeth, can you?' I said.

'I know, but you should have been there when they discovered I'd got Hashimoto's disease as well; it was like they'd found a cure for baldness,' Elaine replied.

'I expect it's because it all proves our identical status,' I said, putting my jacket on; the nights were beginning to get chilly. 'Are you ready?'

'I've been ready for ages.'

Nancy and Kim had told us about a wonderful restaurant. It was further away from the hotel than we usually strayed, but we set off thinking we'd have no problems finding it. Our combined sense of direction being nil, we became hopelessly lost.

'Oh, look Elaine, a Speakeasy. Shall we go in?'

'We most certainly will not,' Elaine replied, in her "I'm-thirty-minutes-older-than-you" voice.

'Why not?'

'Just the word, "Speakeasy", conjures up all sorts of images from bygone eras. I've often wondered what they're like inside.'

'If you go in there you might find more than an era conjured up,' Elaine replied, wittily.

'But it's not the 1930s, and as far as I know prohibition isn't practised anymore,' I said, with derision.

'Very funny Miss Clever, I know alcohol isn't illegal, but shall we just say you might find the clientele a little dubious. In fact, I don't think we're in the right area for this restaurant, it looks a bit seedy to me,' Elaine said, examining the neon clad streets.

'What, worse than Soho?' I couldn't resist saying.

She was laughing. 'Okay, but lets go into this shopping mall and see if we can find out where we are.'

Fortunately there was a policeman, or cop, just coming out so we asked him for directions.

'You're miles away from where you need to be. Gee, you guys are in a bad part o' town. I suggest you follow this road down here,' he pointed, 'which will take you away from this district towards where you want to be.'

'A bad part of town?' We said in alarm.

'Sure are…' he stopped. Scrutinising us he added, 'you've gotta be twins, right?'

'Yes, we're from England taking part in the twin research at Minnesota University,' Elaine explained.

'I knew you guys were English the minute I heard you speak,' he enthused, as if he'd just discovered Einstein's Theory of Relativity.

We chattered for a few minutes and then he wished us a "nice day" and told us to "be careful" before striding off into the sunset.

'See I told you,' Elaine said.

'All right, you win, no Speakeasy for me then.'

Some thirty minutes later, we found the restaurant, the food was great but the portions were so huge that it looked like we'd eaten nothing when the waiters removed our plates. We arrived back at our hotel a little after midnight. Alighting from the elevator, we walked to the end of the long corridor where our room was situated and I inserted the key in the lock. Nothing. I tried again, but it wouldn't open.

'It feels like it's jammed,' I said, turning to Elaine.

'What are you like? Let me do it,' she said, taking the key.

She pushed and pulled, but nothing happened.

'See, you can't do it either, let me have another try.'

As I inserted the key I heard a noise coming from the other side of the door.

'Shhh.'

'What's the matter.'

'I think there's someone in our room.'

'Let me listen. Yes, you're right I can hear somebody moving around.'

'What shall we do?' I whispered.

'I don't know,' she whispered back.

We looked at each other fearfully for long moments.

'Hang on a minute,' Elaine finally said, looking at the number on the door.

'It's the right number,' I said, trying to be helpful.

'Yes, but it's the wrong floor,' she spluttered.

We fell in a heap convulsing with laughter, unable to stop, and the more we tried the harder it became. Eventually, when our hilarity subsided we crept stealthily away from the door, not knowing if the occupants of the room had heard us or not. We scurried to the elevator and made our getaway.

'Can you imagine the headlines. Twins found in drunken disarray in respectable hotel.'

'We're not drunk,' Elaine said.

'I know, but the way we're behaving you'd think we were,' I replied.

'You're right, we wouldn't normally behave like this, would we?'

'Not normally, perhaps it's because we're on our own. We wouldn't dare to in front of the children, they would be ashamed of us.'

'Yes, I can just imagine the distain on Kristy and Sacha's faces.'

'If Lisa and Steven were here, they'd be saying, "Oh, Mum how embarrassing".'

We started laughing again.

Chapter Twenty Six

Relating our escapade the following morning, the team were highly amused, but not the least bit surprised.

'This is the kind of behaviour patterns we've encountered with a lot of twins we've worked with. It stems from not having spent any childhood years together; put simply you're just making up for lost time.' Tom's rationalisation made us feel more at ease about our childish conduct. This time I fully agreed that our behaviour had been juvenile.

'By the way,' he added. 'Don't forget you'll be picked up at seven o'clock tonight, so be ready to party.'

* * *

Tom lived about twenty miles from Minneapolis. A long driveway finally reached the house; an impressive clapboard structure, set in at least two acres of landscaped gardens which rolled down to a glassy lake, where a boat was moored. Stars were appearing in the clear sky, lights blazed from every window and people spilled out onto the veranda.

Tom greeted us.

'Come in, come in and meet everyone,' Tom said, slapping a large badge, which proclaimed M.Z., onto our posh party frocks. 'You must wear this so that everyone knows who you are,' he said.

'Wouldn't our names have done the trick? Elaine said, tongue-in-cheek.

'We need them to know who you really are, tonight you're not Elaine and Mary but our latest M.Z.'s.'

'What does M.Z. mean? We both asked simultaneously.

'It stands for Monozygotic.'

Well we did ask.

Amused by our blank faces, Tom explained, 'Twins like you are developed from the same zygote or fertilised egg, which makes you genetically identical. Fraternal twins are termed Dizygotic or D.Z. twins and are no more genetically alike than siblings born successively.'

'Will all this research be of use to anyone? Elaine asked Tom.

'Definitely. Identical twins are the most sought after subjects for psychological and medical research, particularly ones reared apart, because all their genes are alike, making the genetic variable absent. Eventually, all our findings will be published and we should, by then, be able to ascertain the overriding factor in what makes human beings the way they are. You and Mary have helped us to reach our goal, which should tell us which parts of our behaviour and personality are inherited through our genes, and which are inculcated from our surroundings and early teachings.'

At this point someone thrust drinks in our hands and Tom was off greeting someone else.

We mingled and rubbed shoulders with professors, doctors, lawyers and, it seemed, just about everyone from the university. Our every whim was indulged and we felt like A-list celebrities, they certainly made "their" twins feel unique. All too soon it was time to say goodbye to Tom, to this man who had put us through hell. But we would always remember him with affection and respect.

Back in our blue and gold hotel room, which had served as a womb for ten days, we undressed.

'We met so many distinguished people tonight, I couldn't believe how friendly they were,' I commented.

'Just because they're clever doesn't mean they're not human,' Elaine replied putting cream on her face. 'I talked to so many eminent people tonight and they were all really nice and so interesting. I feel quite guilty for laughing about their names.'

'This trip has been a revelation in more ways than one,' I said. 'Are you pleased we came?'

'Absolutely. You know Tony was right when he said we needed time together. I know we were close before, but now it's different in a way which is hard to put into words,' Elaine replied.

'I understand what you mean, it's as if we never spent thirty years apart and now I realise I don't have to *try* and be you anymore, because I am you,' I said.

Elaine smiled, knowing exactly what I meant.

Nancy Segal   Mary Holmes   Mary Moster   Elaine Allin   Kim Wlicox

Kim, Mary, Elaine, Nancy and Mary
Research team 1984

Mary and Elaine
Minnehaha Falls 1984

Mary Holmes Tom Bouchard Elaine Allin

Chapter Twenty Seven

The following year was a busy twin year. In June we were invited to a twin reunion in Hertfordshire, organised by John Stroud. Then Tom asked if we would like to participate in a television show in Rome. Neither of us had ever visited Rome; it was so exciting. Tony said we were like "professional orphans". In the December, RAI, the National Italian television network, planned to bring twins from all over Italy to participate in a live programme called Domenica En, literally meaning, 'On Sunday'. Tom was bringing the Jim Twins from the States. They had been reunited when they were thirty nine years old and were quite famous in America. Their lives, up until meeting, had been uncannily similar. Not only had they been called Jim by their respective adoptive parents, but their first wives had the same Christian names; as did their children. They both subsequently divorced and their second wives also bore the same name. They had even named their dogs the same when they were children. Our tale was unremarkable in comparison.

RAI flew us out to Rome first class and accommodated everyone in a five-star hotel for five days, it should only have been two days, but Elaine charmed them on the telephone, saying we would love some time to explore their beautiful capital city.

We arrived on the Friday and had rehearsals at the studio on Saturday.

The following day the programme was to go out live and Elaine and I were a little apprehensive. We were assured earpieces would be provided which translated the Italian into English, but nonetheless we were nervous. However, as Elaine pointed out, 'Its not as if anyone in England will see it if we mess up.'

Arriving at the studio on the Sunday morning, we were astounded to see the entire building consumed by twins and triplets. If we hadn't been twins ourselves it would have been intimidating.

We met the Jims, who were both friendly, extrovert and out for a good time. It was difficult at times conversing with them, because of their identical Christian names. But, as we got to know them better we were able to notice the slight differences that all identical twins possess. Elaine, is slightly bigger and taller than me. I often teased her.

'Because you were the biggest baby, you took all the best food and squashed me in the womb.'

'Who told you that?'

'It's a known fact.'

'I love your 'known facts', where did you get that one from?'

'I read it somewhere.'

'Unproven,' she chanted.

Also her face is slightly square, mine more oval and as we'd discovered in America, there were other bits of our bodies which differed.

The television studio was large. The twins were seated in tiers around the set below. Our seats were commonplace, but the set boasted a lavish settee draped in gold, in front of which stood an oblong glass table; it sparkled like an ostentatious diamond under the bright television lights. An arrangement of colour co-ordinating flowers stood tastefully alongside. The setting looked incongruous among the cameras and thick wires which snaked along the floor. On the opposite wall were banks and banks of huge screens, all showing the same picture, the audience of twins. Tom was seated on the front row, because he was important. We were seated a couple of rows behind him.

Just as they warned us all to be quiet and the cameras started to roll, my ear-piece fell out. Overtaken by panic I scrabbled about on the floor. Elaine immediately sensing my plight helped. Fortunately, I retrieved it just in time to see Tom's face replicated on the countless television screens, I hadn't heard his question but he had launched into a lengthy treatise about his work with twins. I relaxed slightly, until that is, I heard our names in the ear-piece and saw my face everywhere. They were asking me a question. Oh God.

I heard the tinny, continental voice say. 'Mary, how did you feel when you first met Elaine?'

The words which gushed from my mouth were unadulterated clichés.

'Oh, it was wonderful, after thirty years of waiting, I couldn't believe it, it was fantastic.'

In my ear-piece all I heard was "fantastica". Then the presenter was asking Elaine how she felt about me. Her face flooded the screens. She had barely finished speaking when there appeared to be a commotion in the studio and people were gesticulating in a significant manner. An announcement was being made, which wasn't being translated. There was a brief delay before we were informed that the World Cup draw was about to take place. It was hard to believe they had gone to all this trouble and then aborted the programme prematurely. Knowing how passionate the Italians are about their football, perhaps it wasn't surprising. Nonetheless, it was an expensive exercise for two sentences. Not that we minded. Happily, we were free to explore the ancient treasures of the eternal city. Elaine was ecstatic, her ear-piece had come loose just as they were asking her question and she'd had to improvise.

Whilst waiting to board our plane to come home, Elaine went to get a drink. When she came back, she was beaming.

'One sentence and I'm a star.'

'What do you mean?' I asked.

'One of the airport workers recognised me and although I didn't totally understand what he was saying, I realised he was telling me he'd seen me on the television.'

'Really? That's amazing. So it's off to Hollywood to make your fortune now you've been discovered,' I teased.

Chapter Twenty Eight

During this period, the newspapers and magazines were awash with stories about twins, particularly twins who had been separated and reunited many years later. *Woman Magazine* telephoned and asked if they could include us in an article they were publishing. John Stroud was also featured. We agreed and Jill Todd came to interview us. The small excerpt about us was satisfactorily written up, although we hated the photograph they had chosen. The photo the *Sunday Mirror* published the subsequent year was even worse of me but it lead to an enigma which we've never been able to solve.

For their Investigative Page, the newspaper was trying to locate the long-lost twin of a forty-two-year woman, who had discovered, only five years previously, of the existence of her twin sister. They believed, by featuring other twins who had found each other, it would help this lady who despaired of ever finding her twin. Again they asked our permission, and said they would use the article from *Woman Magazine*. This they did but included a few syrupy phrases which made us cringe.

"They often hold hands".

"Just to hear each other's voice makes us incredibly happy. Mary says".

"Elaine says. We talk six times a day on the telephone".

Albeit, we did say that when we phoned each other, the conversations were usually lengthy, but six times a day would have been some record even for us. Conversely, they were minor irritations and the good news was that the other twin came forward, so the story had a happy ending.

The following week, while Elaine was at work at the solicitors, the telephone rang and Sacha answered.

'Could I speak to Elaine Allin please?' It was a lady's voice.

'I'm sorry, mummy's at work but she'll be home soon, can I take a message?'

'No thank you, I'll ring back later, Bye.'

Elaine returned from work, but nobody rang.

'What did she sound like, Sacha?'

'She sounded nice.'

'Yes, but did she have an accent?'

'I don't think so.'

'Well, did she sound like she came from here, or did she speak with a southern accent?'

'I can't remember, but she sounded nice.'

'All right darling, I'll wait until she rings back.'

Elaine wondered if it was someone she knew who had seen the article in the newspaper.

The next evening, Elaine was cooking dinner in the kitchen when the telephone rang, again Sacha answered.

'Could I speak to Elaine Allin please?'

'Yes, I'll just get her for you.'

Sacha ran into the kitchen. 'Mummy, Mummy it's the same lady on the phone for you.'

Elaine hurried to the phone. The line was dead. Whoever it had been had hung up.

Elaine rang to tell me what had happened.

'I've been thinking about it. I've been wondering if it might be our real mother. She could have seen the article in the newspaper, thought she would contact us, and then got cold feet at the last minute. What do you think?' Elaine asked.

'You could be right,' I said. 'It makes sense when you think about it, who else would ring you up twice and then put the phone down before you got there?'

'Well I certainly can't think of anyone I know who would do that, and even if it was someone I didn't know, surely they would have spoken to me.' Elaine sighed. 'In hindsight, if only I'd have answered the phone she wouldn't have had time to have second thoughts.'

'You weren't to know, and anyway we could be wrong. Although, I can't think of another explanation. Anyway, let's look on the bright side, she might ring again, I really hope she does,' I said.

'So do I.'

I felt excited and pleased by Elaine's response. I knew she didn't have the same impetus as I had with regard to trying to find our real mother, but it was something that only her and I could share. Two weeks went by. Nothing. We waited, still hoping she would ring. But whoever the mysterious caller was, she never telephoned again.

* * *

The year was tough for Elaine. Her marriage crumbled, and Chris eventually confessed to his affairs. Trying to keep things as amicable as possible for the girls, Elaine agreed to the sale of the large Victorian house where they lived, in order that Chris wouldn't be encumbered with a large mortgage. Elaine, Kristy and Sacha moved to a terrace house and Elaine endeavoured to restore some normality into their lives. Chris made extravagant promises, saying the girls would never want for anything. Ultimately, he paid only half of the maintenance money and to survive she was forced to take him to court. Later he re-married. He was hardly ever available if the girls wanted to see him and inevitably their contact with him grew less and less until it became non-existent.

Motivated by the inexplicable telephone call, I began trying to find out about our real mother. Her temporary address, which was the boarding house, was on my birth certificate. Where our father's name should have been was a blank space. Armed only with her name and this address, Tony and I set off for Leeds. I'm convinced Tony thought he was Sam Spade. But all too soon our hopes were dashed. We found the road, only to be confronted by obstacles. Apart from one lady who lived across the road, there was no one left who remembered. She was very kind and said she had a vague memory of someone having twins. She did tell us, however, that she knew the lady who had owned the boarding house and amazingly, she was still alive. She had outlived her children and the lady was even able to impart the name of the nursing home where she resided.

We hurried there, our spirits uplifted. On arriving, the staff were very helpful but pointed out that she was almost one hundred years old and was suffering from dementia. Undeterred, we sat with her for over an hour. I believed that even with dementia, past events can often be recalled with clarity. I was wrong.

I explained at length the reason for my visit, did she remember someone living in her house, possibly a friend of her daughters, who had twins? Did she know where she went after she left the boarding house? She looked at me blankly. Suddenly she became animated.

'Are we going to a party?' she asked excitedly.

This carried on until finally Tony and I agreed it was hopeless. I felt downhearted. This lady could tell me everything; and yet she could tell me nothing.

Searching the records in Leeds, we drew another blank. We could only assume she had not been born there. The name Cohen is difficult to isolate in a Jewish community; tantamount to searching for someone called Smith. The Jewish children's home and the hospital where we had been born said their records were destroyed after thirty years. We returned home, dispirited and disappointed. I tried to be philosophical; it wasn't the end of the world. I had a lovely family and I had you. Somehow, I still managed to feel rejected for a second time. Perhaps it runs through the human psyche that we always want more.

Chapter Twenty Nine

During the course of his normal police duties, Tony was involved in a serious incident, which left him with degenerative injuries and poor mobility. At 9am he went into work to be told by the police surgeon he would be a liability to the force in his present condition. By 4pm that same day he had no job. He was devastated. I carried on working for a while, until it became evident that I needed to be at home more than we needed the money.

Tony, his jealousy of Elaine long gone, was like a third twin. We spent holidays together which caused gossip, and for fun we even fostered the notion that we were a threesome. Another relationship which bloomed was with Elaine's mum, Lavinia. At this juncture she had been widowed for many years, had suffered two strokes and kept her independence by living in a ground-floor flat and having help. Elaine visited her every day after work, but her time was limited. So I took to popping in to see Lavinia when I visited Elaine. She seemed genuinely pleased to see me, but I felt it was a double-edged sword.

'She would greet me with affection. 'Come in my darling, it's so lovely to see you. I can't believe it's not Elaine walking through the door.'

I would make drinks and she would talk about the past.

'I can't tell you how often Paddy and I wished we'd adopted you both, but at the time our circumstances were so reduced it didn't seem possible. If ever we saw you in town,

Vince and Kev would want to know why we couldn't have had you as well as Elaine, then I felt even worse.'

'Don't worry about it Nan.' She insisted I called her Nan saying that Mrs. Logan sounded so formal. 'It happened a long time ago, and with the war everything was so much more difficult.' I really didn't want her to get upset. The early memories had long since ebbed away and lay powerless like a spent force. But she carried on punishing herself.

'When you were still babies, Mrs. Black would usually ignore me, unless she had you dressed in a new outfit, then she would come over and show you off.'

'Really?' What an odd thing to do,' I replied, even though I wasn't in the least surprised. She ignored most people.

'I used to think so too. You know what was really strange, apart from the fact that she wouldn't let you and Elaine meet or play together, whenever I saw her with you in the pram, she never had Ann with her.'

I *was* surprised to hear this, and wondered if she'd rejected Ann when I was a baby. If that was so, then Ann would have had good reason to resent me, but she hadn't.

Sometimes Nan would ease herself slowly out of the chair and say, 'I must find the photographs.' She would return with overflowing albums.

'Look this is one of Vince when he was in West Side Story, and this is Vince's wife Annie, she has the most beautiful Titian hair.'

Elaine had told me Annie was Vince's second wife. I'd never met either of them, because they lived in London. The first time I met Vince was at Lavinia's funeral. Lavinia was a lovely, warm-hearted person and Elaine was very upset when she died. I always kept a faint hope that I'd convinced her that the decision she and Paddy had made in 1945, had been the right one.

Ann had made contact with me. Mike, her husband, had persuaded her to see me. There was no love lost between him and my mother and as he told Ann, why should our previous amicable relationship be lost forever? Consequently, I'd been seeing Ann for some time without my mother's knowledge. Out of the blue I received a phone call informing me that Mike had died very suddenly of a heart attack. Ann said she wanted me to come to the funeral. I explained gently that it might be better if I stayed away, as it could cause trouble. My mother would be there. I had visions of this provoking more upset for Ann, which was the last thing she needed. But she insisted and reluctantly I agreed.

I was a little apprehensive when we set off, but not cowed. At last I was my own person and felt I could cope. Tony and I were stunned when my mother hailed me as some long lost prodigal daughter, returned to the fold. Introducing me to strangers, she enthused.

'This is my adopted daughter, well, I look on her as my own.'

I couldn't have felt more confused. But more was to come.

Standing on Ann's doorstep as we left, she said, 'Don't leave it so long next time.'

It had been fifteen years since I'd seen her. Perhaps as she'd grown older she had mellowed and regretted our turbulent relationship. On the way home Tony asked me simply, 'What will you do?'

'Well, if she's prepared to put everything behind us, I should probably do the same. I suppose I could give it another try,' I said uncertainly.

'I'm not having you upset again or putting up with shit like you used to, but if it's what you want you know I'm behind you,' Tony said.

I looked at him gratefully. 'Thanks darling, I'll see how it goes.'

The only place it went was round in a full circle, as she began dictating and trying to ruin my life all over again. I walked away for a second time.

Ann later told me she was suffering from Alzheimers. On the day of Mike's funeral she had evidently forgotten she hated me. During the brief period when I assumed my mother had changed, I was hopeful that God had intervened. But all that had intervened was age and disease.

Chapter Thirty

In the Age of Enlightenment, science came to the fore and supplied concrete answers to questions which had previously lain in the hands of God. Because Elaine and I believe that many things are genetically determined, we have found a strange anomaly in our belief in a God, which we often discuss. Our conversations always end ambiguously. Nurture had caused my early life to be dominated by religion. Later, I questioned first my faith in the church and subsequently my belief in a God. Elaine, whose nurture was not over-powered by religion, still believes in some form of supreme being. Shortly after her mum had died, she related a strange phenomenon.

'I was watching television when a small light appeared on the dark mahogany cabinet in the corner, it moved slowly at first then travelled more quickly up the wall onto the ceiling. I assumed it was my watch and took it off, but the light remained constant, sometimes motionless, sometimes darting around the wall. I switched off the television, but the light stayed.'

I was enthralled. 'What do you think it was?'

'I'm convinced it was my mum, she always said she would try to contact me after she died,' she said.

Tony laughed. 'Of course it was Elaine, or perhaps you'd had one drink too many.'

Used to Tony's cynical sense of humour Elaine retorted, 'For your information I'd not even had one drink and the light continued to glow for the best part of two hours.'

I found it fascinating, despite my atheistic beliefs. 'I must admit it sounds strange, I mean, what else could it possibly have been?'

'Exactly, there's no other explanation. I know it sounds weird but I'm convinced it was mum. It's given me so much comfort and I feel happier.'

I could tell it had really affected her. 'That will please her Elaine,' I said.

The light returned intermittently over the next few months and then stopped. Lavinia's task achieved.

Tony remained sceptical and teased Elaine at every opportunity; until I had an eerie experience of my own.

Although I'd been the one of Jewish birth, Tony had for a long time expressed a wish to visit Israel. One year we holidayed there staying near the Red Sea. During our vacation we journeyed to Masada and the Dead Sea. On reaching the summit of Masada the heat was almost unbearable. As I surveyed the sandy red landscape surrounding the turquoise blue of the Dead Sea, itself highlighted by a ring of white crystals, I was stunned and not just by the magnificent vista. 'I've been here before,' I exclaimed.

The scene replicated a recurring dream I'd been having since my early twenties. Tony knew I wasn't fantasising, because over the years I'd described this place to him many times. In the dream I felt immeasurably sad, it was as if I was experiencing the end of the world and I felt troubled for days afterwards. Now, I was so moved by the plight of the Masada Jews who had fought the Romans 2000 years ago, and their ultimate demise; I found myself crying. It was as though I'd been transported back and was experiencing their grief. Since that visit, the dream has never once returned and consequently, I'm a very confused atheist.

The ultimate question Elaine and I ask ourselves frequently is how does religion or religiousness affect identical twins reared apart? Did I turn away from it because it strangled my early years? Does Elaine's belief in a God stem from her freedom of choice?

Chapter Thirty One

Elaine and I didn't expect anymore twin trips, but out of the blue Tom telephoned and said they were doing follow-ups on the twins they had studied ten years previously. There was however, a condition. When possible, Tom had been lending his twins to the Human Nutrition Research Center on Ageing at Tufts University in Boston. If we agreed, it involved spending the first week in Minneapolis before being flown to Boston for the second week. Tom's largesse shone through as he said that Tony could come with us if he participated in some of the mental tests; the physical tests being an impossibility for him because of his failing mobility. Tom assured us that the tests in Minneapolis would be far more relaxed than our first visit, as would Boston. 'Hey, you're old hands, it'll be a piece of cake,' he said.

Time being a great healer, we agreed. Which just proves how wrong time can be.

* * *

Tom met us at the airport and insisted on taking us immediately to The Mall of America. At the time it was the biggest mall ever built. Apart from thousands of shops, bars and restaurants, it also boasted a large funfair. We were so tired we didn't care if it housed the Taj Mahal. The hotel where we'd stayed previously had been razed to the ground and an office building stood in its place. In Britain, every stone stays put for thousands of years, so we were mystified as to why a country with so much space feels the need to tear something down as soon as it reaches its sell-by date. But the American culture is totally different from ours, and that is what makes it unique.

The team had changed. Nancy had gone on to pastures new in California and had been replaced by Meg. Kate, from Seattle, filled Kim's shoes. They were both cordial and hospitable. They took us on a trip up the St Croix River into Wisconsin on a Paddle Steamer, complete with a live Jazz band. It was a wonderful day, assisted by the imbibing of several Tropical Sunrises. The week progressed quite leisurely, as Tom had prophesied. There were two outstanding moments. The first was when a lady working at the university told Tony his "wives" were waiting for him. The second, when a tornado hit Downtown Minneapolis. Our hotel was not small, but we were convinced the powerful wind would blow it away. Unfortunately, we survived to take part in the research in Boston.

* * *

The building belonging to Tufts University which housed the Ageing Research, was not situated in a salubrious district. As we entered I took one look at the security man at the desk and nudged Elaine.

'Look,' I whispered. 'Who does he remind you of?'

'I don't know, who?'

'He's the image of the baddie in that war film, I can't remember what it's called, he pretended to be the good guy but it turned out he was German. Don't you think he looks a bit menacing?' As I spoke he glanced across and smiled. His hair was so blond it looked like he'd dipped his head in bleach. His pale, steely-blue eyes examined our presence carefully.

'He looks perfectly friendly to me. Come on, or he'll wonder what we're whispering about.'

I followed Elaine dutifully, dragging my case.

He took our details, issued us with badges and told us we would be staying on the twelfth floor.

'But you'll have to get off at the eleventh floor and walk up the stairs because the elevator doesn't reach the twelfth,' he told us, through smiling rows of very white teeth.

'I don't like the sound of that,' I muttered darkly, as we entered the lift.

'I must admit it will be a bind with the cases,' Elaine replied.

'No, it's not that, it means than no one will be able to find us.'

'Why not?'

'Don't you see, they won't tell anyone there's another floor, so everyone will think the eleventh floor is the top floor, even Tony won't know what's happened to us.'

Elaine was laughing. 'You've been reading those Robin Cook medical thrillers again, haven't you?'

'Well yes. Even so you must admit it's a bit weird,' I replied.

As we emerged from the lift, there was a faint medicinal aroma and medical devices lined the walls. A reception desk manned by two nurses in immaculate uniforms smiled their welcome. We had to sign a consent form then we were shown to our separate rooms; we were disappointed not to be sharing the same room. They were perfectly acceptable, more like hotel rooms than we'd expected. But then I spotted them.

'Look Elaine, look.' I pointed to the ceiling.

She gazed upwards. 'What?'

'Those round stainless steel things in the ceiling above the bed.'

'What about them?'

'I think they're bugs,' I whispered.

'I don't think so,' she replied.

'Well, what are they then?'

'Probably something to do with the sprinkler system, in case there's a fire.'

I wasn't convinced. 'Actually, I've just thought of a good title for a book, Terror on the Twelfth Floor. What do you think?'

'I think you're mad,' Elaine said, opening the door and returning to her own room.

In the event, I may have been wrong about the bugs, but not totally wrong about their use of surveillance. The en-suite bathrooms hid the revolting truth. The toilet systems were adapted to monitor and analyse everything emitted from our bodies.

* * *

The staff were extremely kind and because we were on loan, we were afforded privileges other residents were not. We were allowed breaks outside, albeit, we had to sign out and sign back in. Each morning we were given a menu to select food for the day. On our first morning we perused the bill of fare with relish.

'It all looks delicious,' Elaine said. 'I don't know what to choose.'

How wrong she was. It didn't matter what we chose, it was all disgusting. Not only was it disgusting, whatever we left, which was usually quite a lot, had to be set aside, analysed and weighed. They would line up forty or fifty plastic beakers, filled with a sickly looking white liquid. We had to taste them all, signal our preferences and tell them what we thought they tasted of. We were too polite to tell them that most tasted like garbage.

They were totally obsessed with taking our vital signs. This had to be done at 6.30 every morning. Our weight, pulse, blood pressure, blood sugar and blood were cogitated over for what seemed like hours. It appeared if a hair was out of place vital signs had to be taken. Although we met Tony each evening, we were not allowed to eat anything else and could only drink water after nine o'clock.

One test, to measure resting energy expenditure, involved us having to lie in bed – this was the good bit – our upper bodies enveloped in a plastic dome, which rose about eight inches above our noses. We were instructed to stay in this position for three hours and remain as still as possible. It sounded great, we could read or watch television, whichever we pleased.

Just before we parted to go to our separate rooms I said to Elaine, 'At least we'll get a rest.'

'I can't wait.'

After being ensconced in bed under the dome for about half an hour, I felt very hot and slightly claustrophobic. My eyes gradually closed, I was awakened immediately by the researcher assigned to me, tickling my feet.

'No, you can't go to sleep Marybeth.' All the staff called me Marybeth.

'Why not? I'm really tired and being under here is making it a hundred times worse.'

He explained. 'The data I'm monitoring will be totally useless if you go to sleep, you have to be awake so your body's resting energy can be observed.'

'Oh, I see.' I didn't see, but then anything technical was a lost cause to me.

With the passing of time I became hotter and hotter. My eyes closed, I was awoken. I wanted to thrash my arms about but I didn't dare. My eyes closed. I was awoken. How many times this happened during the course of the three hours I don't know. I was losing the will to live.

Finally, the dome and monitoring equipment were removed. Exquisite relief.

A nurse entered my room.

'You're next test is in twenty minutes, so you can go outside for a quick break if you want.'

'Oh, thank you, we will.'

I rushed into Elaine's room.

'Come on quick.'

'Why?' She snapped, sitting in front of the mirror combing her hair.

'We can have a quick break, and for goodness sake you haven't got time to do your hair,' I replied heatedly.

We looked at each other realising that Tufts University had managed to do something nothing else ever had. For the first time our relationship had been affected by conflict. It didn't last. Elaine's mouth turned upwards, my sense of humour returned. Amused, we ran down the stairs and dived for the elevator, comparing our identical woes from the torturous three hours.

For the other tests we had to attend hospital. This involved lengthy waits and being inserted into strange machines from which radiation was emitted. Mostly, we signed the consent forms, endured the ordeal then dismissed the episodes from our minds. But the bone density test is memorable, not for medical reasons, but for the young, good looking Bostonian doctor who gave me grounds to tease Elaine.

'"Your sister's bone density is much healthier than yours",' I mimicked.

'Well, there you are then, your theory about me starving you in the womb must be true.' Her eyes twinkled. 'My bone density must have pleased him, look what he gave me.' She held out her hand.

Nestled in the palm of her hand was a heart-shaped chocolate wrapped in gold paper.

'How come I didn't get a chocolate?' I complained.

'Perhaps it's because he preferred my bones to yours,' Elaine replied smugly.

163

'Yeah right, and perhaps it's because he fancies you,' I said.

Forty minutes later we had to undergo another scan, my hypothesis being so he could give Elaine another chocolate; obviously it would look suspicious if he'd not asked to see me as well. Suffice it to say, she came back with another chocolate and I was bereft of sweet-meats.

As the week joyously drew to a close, we planned our strategy for the weekend. We intended to stay at the university on Friday night, but as all the tests were completed we were at liberty to go where we wished. We proposed to visit Salem on Saturday, our last day, but on our first night of freedom, we dressed up and hit Jacob Wirth's Bar; a place Tony had found not far from the university. It had an amazing atmosphere. A wooden bar took up the whole length of one side of the room, dusty wooden floors and a sizable piano for community singing added to the ambience. Elaine and I had a penchant for Baileys Irish Cream. Unfortunately, they had run out so we settled for Tropical Sunrises. The man seated at the piano was playing requests and we all sang along with verve. After imbibing several of the aforementioned Tropical Sunsets, I decided it was time to request a song.

'Hello, can you play 'American Pie' please?' I shouted. It was very noisy.

'I can't hear you.'

I walked unsteadily over to the piano. 'Can you play 'Bye Bye Miss American Pie' please?'

'Well I can, but it's so long and I've found it doesn't always lend itself to community singing,' he replied affably.

I returned disappointedly to my seat. 'I don't see why he can't, it's a great song.'

Elaine and Tony agreed.

'You go and ask him,' I urged Elaine.

'Okay,' she replied.

'He says if he does no one will sing,' Elaine said returning to her seat.

'I'll tell him we'll sing really loudly.' By this time I'd demolished another Tropical Sunset and my inhibitions had joined the dust on the floor.

'Hey, Mr. Piano Man please, please play 'American Pie', we'll make sure everyone sings. Very, very loudly. I promish,' I burbled.

He gave in. As Tony observed, there was little choice. However, vindication was mine as everyone in the place sang out 'Bye Bye Miss American Pie' with gusto.

It was very late when we left. Walking to the door was a major achievement, even with assistance from my other half and my other self. Tony's anxiety penetrated the fog where my brain was located. Hugging him I told him not to worry, we'd had the best night ever. Reluctantly Tony kissed me and Elaine goodnight. Somehow, Elaine managed to haul me into the elevator, past the spymaster – as I called him – and eventually into my bedroom. I fell into bed but did not fall asleep. The room spun, I felt horribly sick. Stultified by alcohol I stumbled blindly to the bathroom. As I was throwing up I thought, with a measure of glee, *analyse that.*

Chapter Thirty Two

Surprisingly, I recovered sufficiently for our trip to Salem the next day. The hot sun blanched the neat white houses beyond white, giving the place a tropical feel, despite its Eastern Seaboard location. We ambled down the quiet streets enjoying the peace. In the museum it was distressing to learn how dreadfully the women and even female children had been treated, accused of being witches on the slightest whim and burnt to death. Later, Elaine and I returned to Tufts to collect our luggage and walked into a crisis.

A nurse rushed over to me.

'We've been looking for you all day Marybeth, where have you been?' She asked worriedly.

'We've been to Salem. Why is there a problem?' Oh, God, was it about me being sick? I was the architect of my own demise, just as I'd been when I was small.

'It's the results of your tests, Doctor Goldberg is waiting. He's interrupted his camping trip especially to see you,' she said, lines furrowing her brow.

Elaine and I exchanged quick glances, wondering what was happening. She ushered me quickly down the corridor into an office marked 'Private'.

The doctor I encountered on the other side of the desk, was tall, dark and tanned.

'Ah Marybeth, at last,' he said.

'I'm sorry if you've been waiting for me, we've been out and I didn't realise there was a problem,' I said meekly.

'Not to worry, you're here now,' he said, studying a file on his desk. 'I guessed there might be complications when I read the form you completed before you left England. Now we have all the results it's worse than I first thought.'

'Why what's wrong?' Alarm churned through me.

'You had a thyroidectemy some years ago, and it appears you're not on any medication. Have you been feeling ill?'

'Not really ill, I haven't been too good for a couple of years now, but my doctor says it's due to the onset of the menopause, so I assumed I'd have to put up with it.'

'Actually, it's nothing to do with the menopause, although age can be a factor. Given that antibodies were discovered at the time of your operation, you should have been monitored. The antibodies work against the natural thyroid function and causes a drop in your thyroxin levels. As you age, the fluctuating hormones worsens the condition. Basically, what is left of your thyroid has gone so under-active that your metabolism has slowed down dramatically. It is affecting every organ in your body, including your heart. Undetected it can be very serious. I'm going to start you on medication immediately, but you will need a much higher dose, so it's imperative you see your own doctor when you arrive home. Also, don't drink alcohol as this could exacerbate your condition,' he concluded, writing out a prescription.

I gulped. Did he know how much I'd drunk last night? Would I die?

'Will I be all right once I'm taking the medication?' I asked tentatively.

'It will take a while for your body to adjust, but when you're on the correct dosage, you should be fine. However, you will have to take it for the rest of your life.'

I felt numb, realising now why they had stopped me from doing some of the physical tests. I felt grateful and guilty simultaneously; not only had I jokingly inferred we were part of

167

some sinister medical plot, we'd both ridiculed their constant taking of vital signs.

'I'm so sorry doctor that you had to come back from your trip, but I can't thank you enough.'

'It's no problem and now it's sorted out. I'll get back; my son will be wondering what's happened to me,' he said, closing up the file on his desk.

I felt ashamed and full of remorse. Even though the intense research had been a chore and the experience often disagreeable; I felt an overwhelming debt of gratitude to Tufts University for their skillful and meticulous care.

Chapter Thirty Three

The thirty year hiatus, although a distant memory, will always be part of who we are. Some people ask if we feel aggrieved by our separation? A potentially ambivalent question to which we both reply with a positive "no". It could be argued that our sanguine stance is misguided and our lives could have been better. It is a sad fact that identical twins were allowed to be separated, which does gives validity to the argument. However, choices were made for us which negate any certainty of how life might have been had we been reared together. We value our first feelings of bonding; they were poignant and real. As children, would we have recognised this special rapport? To this we have no answer. The determination to find each other was delayed by daily existence and circumstances, but our eventual reunion lead to a powerful relationship. Our families tolerate our idiosyncrasies, share our experiences and embrace each of us as their own. I wanted to be you, but the passage of time and identical genes revealed the truth; I am you. Nature had lead us to each other but sometimes it can be cruel.

* * *

The telephone rings, Tony answers.

'It's your womb mate.' A witticism he invented many years ago.

'Hi, I was going to ring you when I'd finished cleaning the kitchen, we've got the theatre tickets for next week.' My love of the theatre had blossomed under Elaine's guidance.

'Great, I might not be able to get down Friday night because I've made an appointment to see the doctor after work. But I'll come on Saturday in plenty of time,' Elaine said.

'It's most likely nothing, but it's best to get it checked,' I replied. A lump had appeared in her breast a few weeks ago. Neither of us worried too much because we'd been there before and they ended up being cysts, or in my case I was told I had lumpy breasts.

'No I'm not worried, but it really hurts so I'll have to get it sorted out.'

I felt relieved. 'Actually if it hurts it won't be anything, because they always say there's no pain with cancerous lumps.'

'Exactly my sentiments.'

We were both wrong. The doctor sent her to the hospital immediately, just to be on the safe side. I wanted to go with her but she said no, she would be fine. She planned to take a couple of hours off work and go back afterwards. She was adamant she didn't want me to travel over for such a short time. I didn't insist, I felt I would be making a big deal out of nothing which would ultimately make her more nervous.

I hovered near the telephone snatching it from its cradle on the first ring.

'Hi, how did it go?'

'It's not good news I'm afraid,' she paused and my heart stopped. 'It's cancer,' Elaine said in a flat voice.

'Oh, Elaine no. Are they sure?' It felt as if someone had hit me in the stomach.

'Even before they did the mammogram and ultrasound scan, the consultant told me starkly he was ninety-five percent sure the lump was malignant. I felt like someone had kicked me in the stomach.'

'I wish you'd have let me come with you, you should never have been on your own.' How could I have been so complacent? I should have insisted.

'I know, I did need you,' her voice wavered, but she didn't cry. Eventually, she continued. 'Even though there was a doubt at the back of my mind that this was different, I still felt optimistic it would turn out to be nothing. When the mammogram didn't pick it up I thought the consultant was wrong, but the ultrasound scan detected it. I was there for a long time because they performed the biopsy straight away. It was extremely painful...' She stopped speaking. I could feel her pain. I wanted to expel it but I was helpless.

'I'm so sorry, Elaine. Have you decided what you're going to do?' We often discussed our opposition to surgery, unless it was absolutely necessary. Largely because friends we'd known throughout our lives, had undergone operations to no avail.

'I've to go back next week and discuss the options with the consultant. What would you do?' Elaine asked.

'Well I know what we've always said Elaine, but they've come a long way with breast cancer research. All those times we've discussed it in the past, it was hypothetical. It changes everything when it's you. If it's the only option open, I think if it was me I'd take it.'

'I knew that would be your answer. Despite some misgivings, I feel it's my only prospect of fighting it,' she replied.

'Good, we'll beat it together. I'm definitely coming to the hospital with you next week, but Tony and I will come over now.' I knew Tony would want to be with her as much as I did. Unfortunately, neither of her daughters lived close by. Kristy was living and working for NIDA in Sydney, Australia, and Sacha worked for a large bank in London.

'No, honestly Mary, I'll be fine, it's too late now, perhaps tomorrow?'

'Are you sure? I could come and stay the night with you.'

'Yes, honestly I'm sure. Don't worry I'll be okay.'

'We'll see you tomorrow.'

When I came off the phone Tony hugged me silently. We said nothing, there was nothing to say. I was crying.

The cancer wasn't in my body, but my mind said otherwise as I groped every step of the tortuous way with you. Memories of the metal nit comb from my childhood came to me uninvited; I wanted to grasp it and scrape away the disease which festered inside you. Sleep evaded me during the weeks that followed, submerged in a bottomless pit from which I seemed unable to crawl. We'd spent thirty years apart and thirty years together, maybe it was all we were allowed. I felt the last thirty years slipping away like the last few grains of sand in an egg-timer; time had run out. Not only were these ideas negative, they were unsupportive and selfish. I seemed incapable of shaking them off, until I realised what was hidden right in front of my eyes. Your spirit. I'd spent years trying to be you and what I'd learned when I finally emerged, was an optimism for life that burned brighter than any star. Your commitment to eliminate the cancer inside you is very potent. I am you, and therefore my allegiance will be equally as fervent.

* * *

You are amazing. After undergoing all the treatment and only five months off work, you look so well it's easy to forget what you've been through. You are even renowned for being the 'lap-dancing' patient of the cancer hospital. The radiotherapy team, clearly preferring the distorted translation of tap dancing.

Last night you said to me.
'I've decided to live one day at a time and enjoy it. Let's face it, everyone exists on the edge of life.'
Being you, I agreed.

Elaine and Mary together